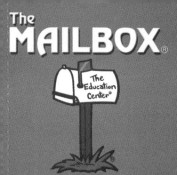

The MAILBOX®

The Education Center®

Math Choose & Do Grids

MW00651956

Over 375 Differentiated Activities

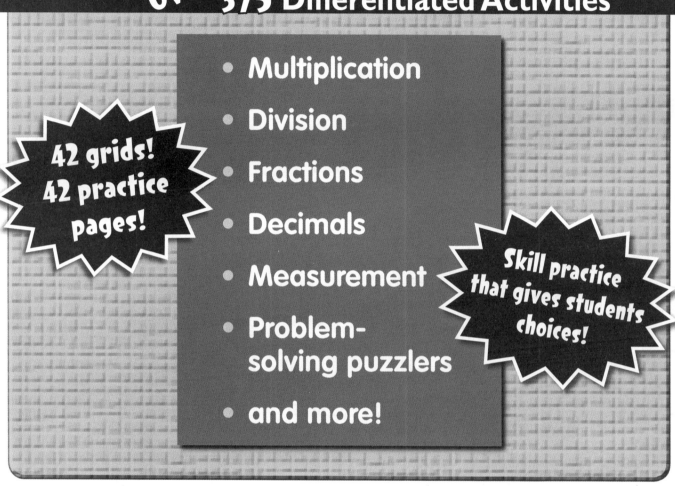

42 grids!
42 practice pages!

- **Multiplication**
- **Division**
- **Fractions**
- **Decimals**
- **Measurement**
- **Problem-solving puzzlers**
- **and more!**

Skill practice that gives students choices!

Managing Editor: Sherry McGregor

Editorial Team: Becky S. Andrews, Debbie Ashworth, Diane Badden, Kimberley Bruck, Karen A. Brudnak, Pam Crane, Chris Curry, Colleen Dabney, David Drews, Ann E. Fisher, Kelli Gowdy, Tazmen Hansen, Marsha Heim, Lori Z. Henry, Troy Lawrence, Kitty Lowrance, Jennifer Otter, Mark Rainey, Greg D. Rieves, Hope Rodgers-Medina, Rebecca Saunders, Donna K. Teal, Sharon M. Tresino, Zane Williard

www.themailbox.com

©2012 The Mailbox® Books
All rights reserved.
ISBN 978-1-61276-211-1

Printed in the United States
10 9 8 7 6 5 4 3 2 1

HPS233480

What's

42 Activity Grids
Nine choices on every grid!

Two simple steps!

1. **Program** the student directions.
2. **Copy** the grid and its practice page.

Address different learning levels and styles with a single grid!

≡ Identifying Plane and Solid Figures ≡

Name _____

Date _____

Choose ___ or more activities to do.
When you finish an activity, color its number.

1 Draw a "geom-e-tree." Label the tree trunk "Plane Figures." Draw five or more branches on the tree. Then label each branch with the name of a different plane figure. On each branch, draw four or more leaves and write a different attribute of the figure on each one.	**2** Cut six same-size paper triangles. On each one, draw a different solid figure and label it and its base, vertices, edges, and faces. Then staple your triangles together to create a banner. 	**3** Use a ruler to draw a net for each figure. A. triangular prism B. cylinder C. rectangular pyramid D. rectangular prism 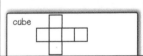
4 Cut out 20 examples of solid figures from old magazines or newspapers. Sort them into four categories according to their attributes. Then glue each category of shapes to a different piece of paper and describe the category on the paper's flip side.	**5** Do the practice page "Up Close!" 	**6** Make a list of two or more real-world examples of each figure. **triangular pyramid** **triangle** **triangular prism** **cone** **square pyramid**
7 Describe the plane figure or figures that make up the faces of each solid figure. A. cube B. cylinder C. rectangular pyramid D. rectangular prism E. triangular prism	**8** Research the state flags of the United States. Choose ten flags that each have at least one plane figure. Write the name of each state and describe the geometric figures on each flag.	**9** Use the vertices to name each edge and face of Figures 1 and 2. **Figure 1** **Figure 2**  Figure 1 Edge: HI Face: HIJ

Choose & Do Math Grids • ©The Mailbox® Books • TEC61229 • Key p. 94

Note to the teacher: Program the student directions with the number of activities to be completed. Then copy the page and page 62 (back-to-back if desired) for each student.

61

Inside

42 Practice Pages
Always activity 5 on the grid

Identifying Plane and Solid Figures

Name _____ Date _____

Up Close!

Name each figure.
Write your answer in the puzzle.
Then write each circled letter on its matching numbered line or lines to complete the statement.

Without ___ ___ ___ ___ ___ ___ ___ ___ ,
         12 5   4   9   5 15   8 16

___ ___ ___ ___ would be
 9 10 15   3

" ___ ___ ___ ___ ___ - ___ ___ ___ ___ ___ !"
  11 4   6   7 15   2   5 14 13

Tip!
To save paper, copy a grid and its practice page back-to-back!

Word Bank

circle	hexagon	prism	sphere
cone	octagon	pyramid	square
cube	parallelogram	rectangle	trapezoid
cylinder	pentagon	rhombus	triangle

Choose & Do Math Grids • ©The Mailbox® Books • TEC...

62   **Note to the teacher:** Use with page 61.

Independent practice for
- Morning work
- Center work
- Homework
- Free time
- Anytime

Answer keys on pages 89–96.

Table of Contents

Place Value to Millions

Name _____

Date _____

Choose ___ or more activities to do.
When you finish an activity, color its number.

---

1 Add a digit to complete each number below. Then write each number in word form and expanded form.

3,_58
2,46_
_57,849
2,53_,574

---

2 Round **807,564** to each of the following places:

- millions
- hundred thousands
- ten thousands
- thousands
- hundreds
- tens

---

3 Write a six-digit number and spin the spinner. Write the symbol next to your number. Then write a six-digit number to correctly complete the statement. Repeat five more times.

---

4 Use the digits 2–8 to write four different seven-digit numbers. Arrange the digits so that each one has a different value in each number. Then circle the **5** in each number and name its place value.

2 3 4 5 6 7 8

---

5 Do the practice page "Stash 'n' Dash."

---

6 Find the riddle's answer. Write it in standard form. Then write and solve a place value riddle of your own.

I am an odd number.
I am less than ten thousand but greater than nine thousand, nine hundred ninety-seven.
What am I?

---

7 Identify the pattern in each number series. Then write the next three numbers.

A. 2,765; 2,865; 2,965…

B. 435,250; 445,250; 455,250…

C. 599,999; 699,999; 799,999…

D. 2,050,000; 1,950,000; 1,850,000…

---

8 Write four seven-digit numbers. Then use the code to draw each one.

● = 1
■ = 10
▲ = 100
○ = 1,000
□ = 10,000
△ = 100,000
▣ = 1,000,000

---

9 Write the numbers shown in order from least to greatest.

474,216	474,316
436,084	4,156,320
456,320	47,421
446,412	474,000
4,742	474,210

Note to the teacher: Program the student directions with the number of activities to be completed. Then copy the page and page 6 (back-to-back if desired) for each student.

Place Value to Millions

Name ______________________________ Date ______________

Stash 'n' Dash

I. Color each number disc according to the code.

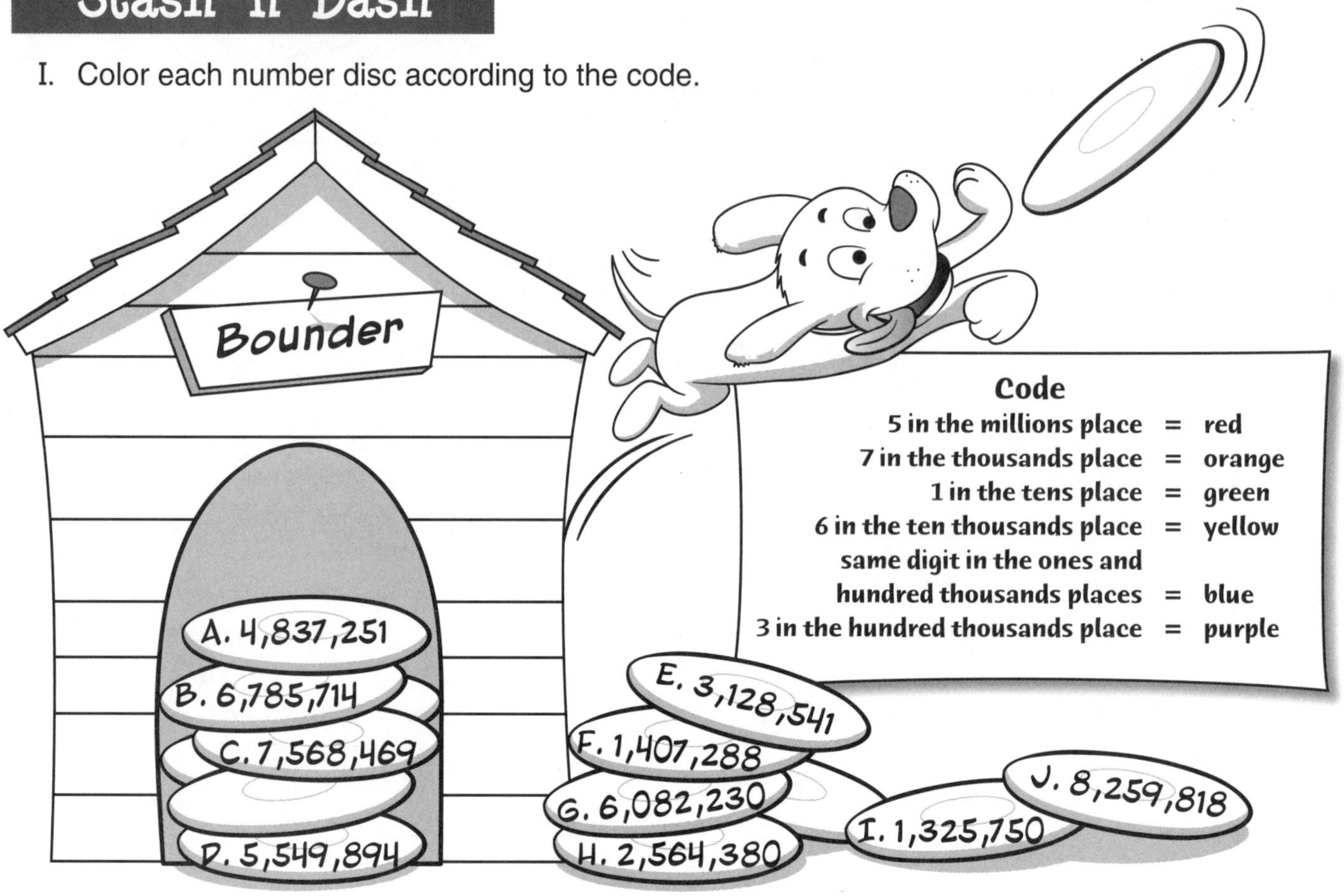

Bounder
A. 4,837,251
B. 6,785,714
C. 7,568,469
D. 5,549,894
E. 3,128,541
F. 1,407,288
G. 6,082,230
H. 2,564,380
I. 1,325,750
J. 8,259,818

Code

5 in the millions place	=	red
7 in the thousands place	=	orange
1 in the tens place	=	green
6 in the ten thousands place	=	yellow
same digit in the ones and hundred thousands places	=	blue
3 in the hundred thousands place	=	purple

II. Arrange the numbers in order from least to greatest by writing each letter in the appropriate box.

least									greatest

III. A. Write the largest number in expanded form. ______________________________

____

B. Write the smallest number in word form. ______________________________

____

C. Write the number with the most odd digits in expanded form. ______________________

____

____

 Note to the teacher: Use with page 5.

Addition of Whole Numbers

Name _____

Date _____

Choose ___ or more activities to do.
When you finish an activity, color its number.

---

1 Write and then solve five different addition problems using the number in the center.

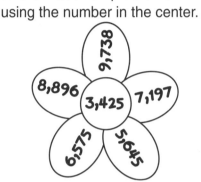

2 Write four addition problems with sums that are greater than 10,000 but less than 15,000. Then write four addition problems with sums that are less than 5,000 but greater than 2,500.

3 Copy the diagram. Then fill in the missing numbers.

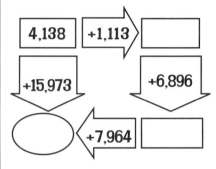

---

4 Use addition to find the missing number in each problem. Then write the complete equation. Subtract to check your answer.

A. ___ – 543 = 443
B. ___ – 710 = 6,618
C. ___ – 436 = 55
D. ___ – 29,029 = 784
E. ___ – 56,628 = 14,907
F. ___ – 964 = 7,307

5 Do the practice page "Packed and Stacked."

6 Estimate each problem's sum by rounding. Next, estimate the sum using front-end estimation. Then solve the problem. Which estimate is more helpful? Explain.

A.   4,830
      2,918
   + 1,621

B.   5,134
        974
   + 6,723

---

7 Copy and complete each chart.

	Add 999.		Add 5,879.
698		543	
710		685	
328		815	
436		491	

8 Use the amounts on the tags to write and solve eight addition problems.

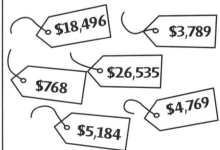

$18,496 $3,789 $26,535 $768 $4,769 $5,184

9 To make each problem correct, rearrange the digits in one addend.

A. 43,210 + 68,547 = 88,888

B. 23,954 + 45,605 = 80,008

C. 73,769 + 20,841 = 98,777

Choose & Do Math Grids • ©The Mailbox® Books • TEC61229 • Key p. 89

Note to the teacher: Program the student directions with the number of activities to be completed. Then copy the page and page 8 (back-to-back if desired) for each student.

Name _____

Date _____

Addition of Whole Numbers

Packed and Stacked

Add. Then use the sums to complete the puzzle.

Across

A. 654
  + 617

E. 37,538
  + 64,447

H. 7,971
  + 890

I. 4,496
  + 671

K. 3,227
  + 887

M. 329
  + 128

O. 568
  + 235

P. 78,941
  + 16,396

Q. 4,814
  + 53,392

Down

A. 82,392
  + 26,153

B. 141
  + 575

C. 856
  + 158

D. 174
  + 282

F. 89,756
  + 5,349

G. 73,846
  + 7,587

J. 71,823
  + 4,456

L. 9,328
  + 9,578

N. 3,659
  + 3,523

Note to the teacher: Use with page 7.

Subtraction of Whole Numbers

Name _____

Date _____

Choose ___ or more activities to do.
When you finish an activity, color its number.

1 Use the pattern shown to write and solve nine subtraction problems.
 	
$1,000 - 111 = n$
$2,000 - 222 = n$
$3,000 - 333 = n$
	2 Draw a Venn diagram and compare subtracting without regrouping and subtracting with regrouping.
	
	Subtraction
	No Regrouping Regrouping
		3 Copy the code and then complete it using five different digits. Then solve each problem.
		
		Code
		♡ = □ = △ =
		☆ = ☺ = # = 0
		
		A. ♡ # # # B. □ # △ #
		  − □☺△ − ☆♡☺
		C. ☆ # ☺ # D. ☺△ # #
		  − ♡□△ − ☆□♡

4 Create a mini poster that shows and explains how to solve the problem shown. 4,000 − 3,898	**5** Do the practice page "On the Spot."	**6** Write four subtraction problems that have the characteristics shown. • The minuend has three, four, or five digits. • The subtrahend has three, four, or five digits. • All the minuend's and subtrahend's digits are odd. • The difference includes even and odd digits.
7 Use consecutive digits to write and solve three subtraction problems. Write a three-, four-, and five-digit problem. $654 - 567 = n$	**8** Estimate each difference. Then solve each problem. After that, arrange the differences from least to greatest. A. $732 - 268 = n$ B. $854 - 309 = n$ C. $4,597 - 3,488 = n$ D. $20,461 - 17,895 = n$ E. $6,053 - 5,320 = n$	**9** Write an acrostic poem about subtraction. S _____ U _____ B _____ T _____ R _____ A _____ C _____ T _____ I _____ O _____ N _____

Choose & Do Math Grids • ©The Mailbox® Books • TEC61229 • Key p. 89

Note to the teacher: Program the student directions with the number of activities to be completed. Then copy the page and page 10 (back-to-back if desired) for each student.

9

Subtraction of Whole Numbers

Name _____   Date _____

On the Spot

I. Estimate each difference. Then subtract and cross out the matching difference below. Four differences will not be crossed out.

(1) 7,000 – 5,269 = _____

(2) 5,804 – 3,917 = _____

(3) 972 – 425 = _____

(4) 7,840 – 2,398 = _____

(5) 14,377 – 5,481 = _____

(6) 23,511 – 19,686 = _____

(7) 844 – 279 = _____

(8) 9,923 – 8,874 = _____

(9) 12,800 – 7,540 = _____

(10) 8,483 – 1,278 = _____

II. Write each number you did not cross out in an oval. Then write a subtraction problem to match.

11. _____ – _____ = ⬭

12. _____ – _____ = ⬭

13. _____ – _____ = ⬭

14. _____ – _____ = ⬭

5,191

547   1,049   8,896

13,702   3,825

7,205   1,887   1,731   182

5,442   565   5,260

456

Multiplication
Three Digits by One Digit

Name _____

Date _____

Choose ___ or more activities to do.
When you finish an activity, color its number.

---

1 | Multiply the numbers in each row, column, and diagonal by the number in the center of the row, column or diagonal. You will have eight problems.

3	8	4
6	9	7
1	5	2

Example: 392 x 9

---

2 | Write and solve 4 three-digit by one-digit multiplication problems using the numbers shown.

212　　　2　　　656

4　　　545　　　5

636　　　3　　　181

7　　　272　　　8

---

3 | Write a three-digit by one-digit multiplication problem that will have a product with all even digits. Then write a three-digit by one-digit multiplication problem that will have a product with only odd digits. The one-digit number must be greater than 2.

---

4 | What is the most important step to remember about multiplying a three-digit factor by a one-digit factor? Create a commercial that will help other students remember this important step.

Remember this!

---

5 | Do the practice page "One Step at a Time."

---

6 | Write a three-digit by one-digit multiplication problem to match each clue.

A. The product ends with a 5.

B. The product ends with a 0.

C. The product ends with a 9.

D. The product begins with a 4.

E. The product begins with a 6.

F. The product begins with a 2.

---

7 | Use the digits in your phone number to create and solve six different three-digit by one-digit multiplication problems.

8 | Multiply each of the following by a number between five and ten.

- number of days in a school year
- total number of days in October, November, and December
- number of pages in your math textbook
- total number of Saturdays and Sundays in a year

---

9 | Draw a diagram that explains how to find the product of a three-digit number multiplied by a one-digit number.

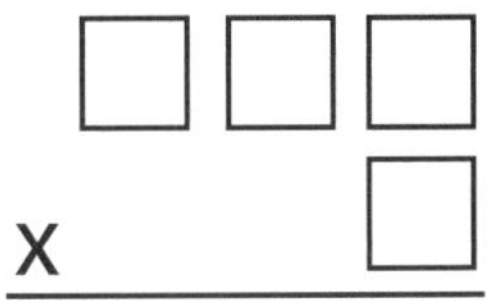

☐ ☐ ☐

X _____ ☐

Choose & Do Math Grids • ©The Mailbox® Books • TEC61229 • Key p. 89

Note to the teacher: Program the student directions with the number of activities to be completed. Then copy the page and page 12 (back-to-back if desired) for each student.

11

Name _____ Date _____

Multiplication
Three Digits by One Digit

One Step at a Time

Solve each problem.

(1) 984
x 6
___ = C

(2) 758
x 5
___ = T

(3) 367
x 4
___ = A

(4) 909
x 8
___ = O

(5) 136
x 3
___ = S

(6) 229
x 7
___ = K

(7) 579
x 2
___ = W

(8) 254
x 8
___ = C

(9) 867
x 6
___ = L

(10) 679
x 9
___ = Y

(11) 678
x 3
___ = I

(12) 498
x 4
___ = O

(13) 743
x 5
___ = S

(14) 950
x 9
___ = D

(15) 289
x 6
___ = H

(16) 627
x 7
___ = B

Why did Janet walk to school backward?

To solve the riddle, write each letter on its matching numbered line or lines.

2,034 3,790   3,790 7,272   3,715   5,904   1,734   1,158   1,468   408   1,992   7,272   5,202   4,389   1,468   2,032   8,550   1,468   6,111

Choose & Do Math Grids • ©The Mailbox® Books • TEC61229 • Key p. 89

Note to the teacher: Use with page 11.

Multiplying
Two Digits by Two Digits

Name _____

Date _____

Choose ____ or more activities to do.
When you finish an activity, color its number.

1 Circle each mistake. Then rewrite each problem and solve it correctly. **A.** 25 x 39 185 + 75 160 **B.** 18 x 42 216 + 432 648	**2** Estimate which problem will have the largest product. Solve to find out. Ⓐ 49 x 37 Ⓑ 69 x 17 Ⓒ 59 x 27 Ⓓ 29 x 47	**3** Copy each problem. Then find the missing numbers. Show your work. **A.** 3☐ x ☐4 2,048 **B.** ☐5 x 2☐ 1,155 **C.** ☐8 x 6☐ 3,024 **D.** 9☐ x ☐1 2,821

4 Find each product.

A. weeks in a year times hours in a day

B. inches in a yard times months in a year

C. days in January times seconds in a minute

D. ounces in a pound times letters in the alphabet

5 Do the practice page "One Every Day?"

6 Use the code to write each factor. Then solve each problem.

Code
5	1	3
2	7	8
6	9	4

A. ⌐⌐ x ☐⌐ = 65 x 89 =

B. ⌐⌐ x ⌐⌐ =

C. ☐⌐ x ⌐⌐ =

D. ⌐⌐ x ⌐⌐ =

7 Farmer Joe can plow 10 square feet in one minute. Which field will take him longer to plow? Explain how you know.

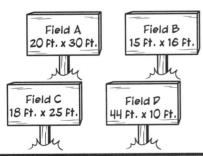

8 Which of these problems have the same products?

12 x 48   32 x 63

56 x 31

24 x 24   22 x 26

9 Use the numbers on the apples to write and solve five different multiplication problems.

Note to the teacher: Program the student directions with the number of activities to be completed. Then copy the page and page 14 (back-to-back if desired) for each student.

Multiplying Two Digits by Two Digits

Name _____

Date _____

One Every Day?

Solve each problem. Show your work.
Shade the box that matches the product.

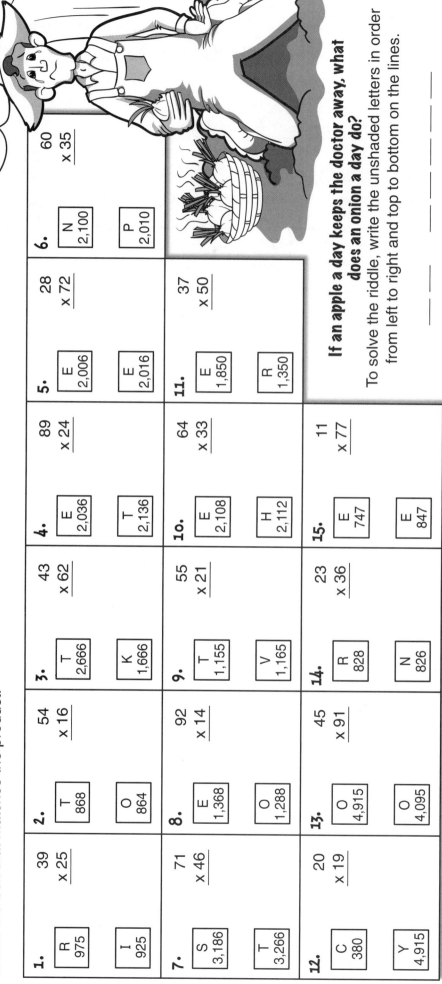

1.

39
x 25

R	I
975	925

2.

54
x 16

T	O
868	864

3.

43
x 62

T	K
2,666	1,666

4.

89
x 24

E	T
2,036	2,136

5.

28
x 72

E	E
2,006	2,016

6.

60
x 35

N	P
2,100	2,010

7.

71
x 46

S	T
3,186	3,266

8.

92
x 14

E	O
1,368	1,288

9.

55
x 21

T	V
1,155	1,165

10.

64
x 33

E	H
2,108	2,112

11.

37
x 50

E	R
1,850	1,350

12.

20
x 19

C	Y
380	4,915

13.

45
x 91

O	O
4,915	4,095

14.

23
x 36

R	N
828	826

15.

11
x 77

E	E
747	847

If an apple a day keeps the doctor away, what does an onion a day do?

To solve the riddle, write the unshaded letters in order from left to right and top to bottom on the lines.

_____ _____ _____ _____ _____ _____ _____ _____ away!

Choose & Do Math Grids • ©The Mailbox® Books • TEC61229 • Key p. 89

Note to the teacher: Use with page 13.

Multiplying
Three or Four Digits by Two Digits

Name _____

Date _____

Choose ___ or more activities to do.
When you finish an activity, color its number.

---

1 Make six different three-digit numbers using 5, 2, and 1. Then multiply each number by 48.

2 Match each problem with its expanded product.

| 206 × 32 | 407 × 18 | 333 × 25 | 124 × 13 |

A. 1,000 + 600 + 10 + 2
B. 8,000 + 300 + 20 + 5
C. 6,000 + 500 + 90 + 2
D. 7,000 + 300 + 20 + 6

3 Roll a die and record your roll. Repeat three times to write a four-digit number. Then roll the die twice and write a two-digit number. Multiply. Repeat the activity five more times.

---

4 Write each problem according to the code. Then solve.

Number Code
◯ = 6   □ = 9   △ = 3   ♡ = 5

A. ◯□♡ × △◯ =
B. △♡◯ × □△ =
C. ♡,□◯◯♡ × ◯□ =
D. △,□◯♡□ × ◯◯ =

5 Do the practice page "Slam Dunk!"

6 Use the digits in the circle to complete each problem. Show your work.

(6 5
  9 3)

A.
□,□0□
× __ □8
_____
247,342

B.
□,□8□
× __ □0
_____
323,340

---

7 Which number shown when multiplied by 327 will equal a product closest to 25,000?

71
68
76
83
80

8 In each problem, one digit is incorrect. Cross it out and write the correct digit above it.

| A. 846 × 30 (²) = 16,920 | B. 145 × 18 = 4,610 |
| C. 383 × 23 = 8,832 | D. 783 × 35 = 28,188 |

9 Decide whether >, <, or = belongs in each circle. Show your work.

A. 408 × 12 ◯ 204 × 24

B. 1,369 × 57 ◯ 2,576 × 39

C. 5,273 × 48 ◯ 4,728 × 18

Choose & Do Math Grids • ©The Mailbox® Books • TEC61229 • Key p. 89

Note to the teacher: Program the student directions with the number of activities to be completed. Then copy the page and page 16 (back-to-back if desired) for each student.

15

Multiplying

Three or Four Digits by Two Digits

Name _____   Date _____

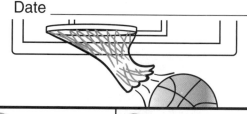

Slam Dunk!

Solve each problem.

A 872 x 28	**B** 456 x 94	**C** 1,007 x 69

D 179 x 33	**E** 271 x 19

H 196 x 29	**I** 3,129 x 18	**L** 512 x 27

O 2,048 x 41	**R** 613 x 50

S 336 x 34	**T** 523 x 42

U 453 x 16	**V** 257 x 64

Why does the basketball coach always carry a towel during a game?
To solve the riddle, write each letter on its matching numbered line or lines.

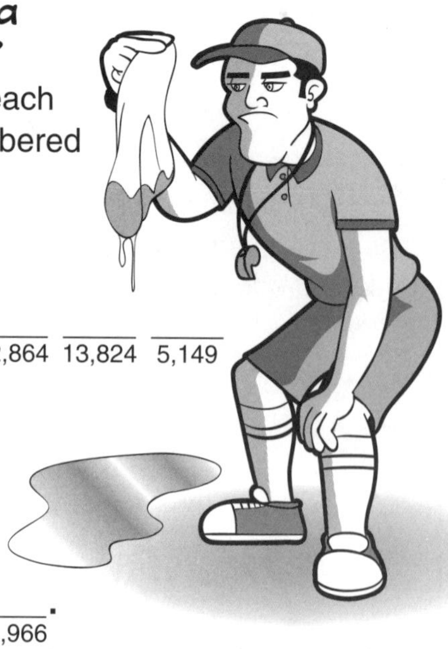

Because his players

5,907 30,650 56,322 42,864 42,864 13,824 5,149

24,416 13,824 13,824

83,968 16,448 5,149 30,650

21,966 5,684 5,149

69,483 83,968 7,248 30,650 21,966 .

Dividing
Three Digits by One Digit

Name _____

Date _____

Choose ___ or more activities to do.
When you finish an activity, color its number.

1 Create a poster that shows how to tell if a number is divisible by 2, 3, 5, or 10. **2 5** **3 10**	**2** Divide. Write each step in a different color. A. $3\overline{)462}$ B. $5\overline{)690}$ C. $4\overline{)583}$	**3** Find the value of each symbol in the problem below. Next, use the symbols to write a new problem and then solve it. $\begin{array}{r} 2\,\text{☆}\,\text{R7} \\ 9\overline{)\square 68} \\ -18 \\ \hline \triangle 8 \\ -8\bigcirc \\ \hline 7 \end{array}$
4 Find the mistakes in these problems. Then make the corrections. $\begin{array}{r} 702 \\ 3\overline{)218} \\ -21 \\ \hline 08 \\ -6 \\ \hline 2 \end{array}$ $\quad$ $\begin{array}{r} 111 \\ 6\overline{)715} \\ -6 \\ \hline 11 \\ -6 \\ \hline 5 \end{array}$	**5** Do the practice page "Topsy-Turvy." 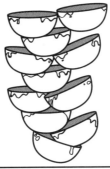	**6** Use the number cards from a deck of cards. Remove the tens and shuffle the cards. Take the top four cards and place them in a row. Use the first card as the divisor and the remaining three cards as the dividend. Write the problem on your paper and solve it. Repeat three times.
7 Divide the number 780 four different times. Use the digits 2, 4, 6, and 8 as the divisors. Circle the problem with a remainder. Then draw a conclusion about that problem.	**8** Spin the spinner. Use the first number you spin as the divisor. Use the next three numbers you spin as the dividend. Divide. Repeat to write and solve four more problems. 	**9** Predict which problem's quotient will not include a remainder. Then solve each problem to find out. A. $627 \div 9 =$ B. $562 \div 4 =$ C. $375 \div 3 =$ D. $439 \div 6 =$

Choose & Do Math Grids • ©The Mailbox® Books • TEC61229 • Key p. 90

Note to the teacher: Each student needs a deck of cards to complete activity 6 and a paper clip to complete activity 8. Program the student directions with the number of activities to be completed. Then copy the page and page 18 (back-to-back if desired) for each student.

Name _____   Date _____

Topsy-Turvy

For each item, use the four digits to write two different division problems—one that will result in the greatest quotient possible and one that will result in the smallest quotient possible.

Then solve each problem and cross out the matching quotients. Show your work on another sheet of paper.

Example:

Greatest		Least
324 R2 3)974 − 9 07 − 6 14 − 12 2	**4 9 3 7**	38 R5 9)347 − 27 77 − 72 5

Greatest		Least
	A 3 8 2 6	
	B 6 1 7 4	
	C 5 4 9 5	
	D 2 1 3 7	
	E 4 3 8 6	
	F 8 2 7 3	

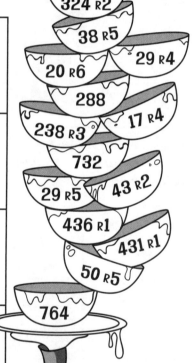

324 R2
38 R5
29 R4
20 R6
288
17 R4
238 R3
732
29 R5
43 R2
436 R1
431 R1
50 R5
764

Dividing

Three Digits by One or Two Digits

Name _____

Date _____

Choose ___ or more activities to do.
When you finish an activity, color its number.

---

1 Which sets of test scores have an average of 90?

> Hint: To find the average of each set of scores, add the scores and divide by 3.

A. 90, 98, 80
B. 98, 86, 95
C. 100, 85, 85
D. 75, 98, 97
E. 83, 93, 94

---

2 If three friends share the cost of these activities equally, how much will each person spend in all? Explain.

Dinner: $42.00
Movie: $34.00
Arcade: $14.00
Bowling: $31.00
Roller-skating: $17.00

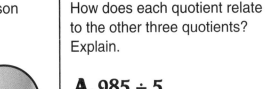

---

3 Solve each problem and then compare the quotients. How does each quotient relate to the other three quotients? Explain.

A. $985 \div 5$
B. $985 \div 10$
C. $985 \div 20$

---

4 The PTA raised $935 for new playground equipment. If each classroom that participated raised at least $60, how many classrooms chipped in, 15 or 16? Explain.

---

5 Do the practice page "Splash to the Finish."

---

6 For each dividend, name the divisor that will result in a quotient of 96.

Dividend	Divisor
2,208 ·	· 11
1,056 ·	· 37
3,840 ·	· 23
5,280 ·	· 40
3,552 ·	· 55

---

7 Four people are sweeping 88 classrooms. It takes ten minutes to sweep each room. If the work is divided evenly, how long does each person work? Explain.

---

8 Find the number that completes each problem.

A. $312 \div n = 78$
B. $256 \div n = 64$
C. $172 \div n = 43$
D. $220 \div n = 55$
E. $364 \div n = 91$

---

9 Divide. Then arrange the quotients in order from smallest to largest.

A. $366 \div 16 =$
B. $387 \div 28 =$
C. $602 \div 15 =$
D. $931 \div 37 =$
E. $854 \div 42 =$

Choose & Do Math Grids • ©The Mailbox® Books • TEC61229 • Key p. 90

Note to the teacher: Program the student directions with the number of activities to be completed. Then copy the page and page 20 (back-to-back if desired) for each student.

Name _____

Date _____

Dividing Three Digits by One or Two Digits

Splash to the Finish

Solve each problem.
To find out which swimmer wins, count the number of quotients in each lane without remainders. The winner has the most quotients without remainders.

Lane 1 	$3\overline{)513}$	$39\overline{)439}$	$5\overline{)218}$	$51\overline{)319}$
Lane 2 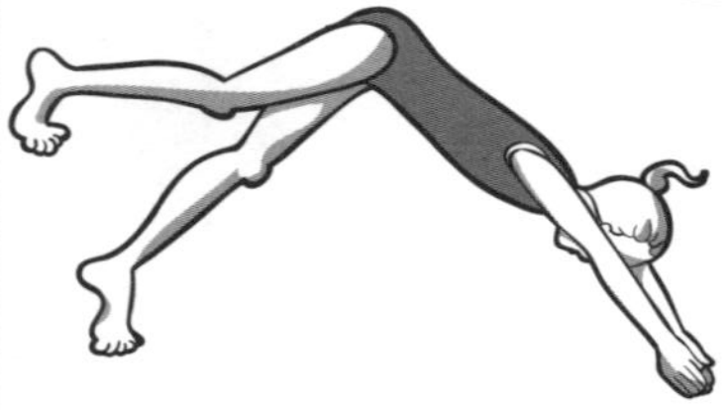	$42\overline{)630}$	$6\overline{)726}$	$57\overline{)294}$	$5\overline{)432}$
Lane 3 	$4\overline{)516}$	$25\overline{)812}$	$3\overline{)294}$	$64\overline{)768}$

Choose & Do Math Grids • ©The Mailbox® Books • TEC61229 • Key p. 90

Note to the teacher: Use with page 19.

Name _____

Date _____

Choose ____ or more activities to do.
When you finish an activity, color its number.

---

1 Solve the division problem shown. Then write and solve four more problems by replacing each digit in the divisor and the dividend with the next consecutive number.

$$5)\overline{2,351}$$

(Hint: $6)\overline{3,462}$ comes next.)

2 Write and solve eight division problems. Use the vertical numbers as the divisors and the horizontal numbers as the dividends.

2	4	1	5
5	3	6	7

$2,415 \div 25$

3 Using the digits shown, write the four-digit dividend and two-digit divisor that will have the largest possible quotient. Then rearrange the digits to write the four-digit dividend and two-digit divisor that will have the smallest possible quotient.

2   3   4
   6   7   5

4 Which two problems do you think will have remainders? Explain your choices. Then solve to find out.

$2,565 \div 5$

$5,439 \div 8$

$4,159 \div 3$

$8,472 \div 6$

5 Do the practice page "'Alakazam!'"

6 Fill in the missing digits to complete each problem.

A $\dfrac{640}{13)\overline{8,\square20}}$

B $\dfrac{620}{16)\overline{9,9\square0}}$

C $\dfrac{308\,R8}{29)\overline{\square,940}}$

D $\dfrac{309\,R13}{22)\overline{\square,811}}$

7 Copy and complete the table.

	Divide by ____.
8,190	
4875	125
9,360	
9,750	

8 Solve each problem. All the quotients have something in common. What is it?

A. $8,976 \div 3 = n$

B. $3,472 \div 8 = n$

C. $5,634 \div 9 = n$

D. $1,624 \div 7 = n$

E. $4,242 \div 21 = n$

F. $2,483 \div 13 = n$

9 Use the numbers to write five different division problems. Then solve each one. Finally, circle the largest quotient and underline the smallest one.

17   5,880

2,520   35   24

49   8,375

Note to the teacher: Program the student directions with the number of activities to be completed. Then copy the page and page 22 (back-to-back if desired) for each student.

Name _____ Date _____

"Alakazam!"

Solve.

1 9)7,506   **2** 7)1,113   **3** 8)5,376

4 12)7,416   **5** 11)8,283   **6** 6)1,764

7 21)3,465   **8** 4)3,360   **9** 15)4,905

Where is that rabbit?

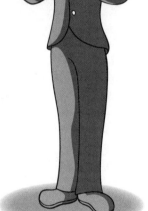

Write each quotient in the magic square. If you are correct, the sum of each row, column, and diagonal should equal the magic sum.

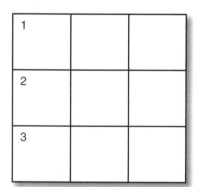

1		
2		
3		

Magic sum: 15

4		
5		
6		

Magic sum: 15

7		
8		
9		

Magic sum: 12

Choose & Do Math Grids • ©The Mailbox® Books • TEC61229 • Key p. 90

Fraction Basics

Name _____

Date _____

Choose ____ or more activities to do.
When you finish an activity, color its number.

---

1 Draw three different pizzas to match the descriptions below.

A. Show $\frac{1}{3}$ of a pepperoni pizza.

B. Show $\frac{3}{8}$ of a cheese pizza.

C. Show $\frac{5}{6}$ of a mushroom pizza.

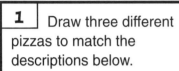

---

2 Fill in the boxes to make the statement true. Repeat nine more times.

$$\frac{\Box}{\Box} < \frac{1}{2} < \frac{\Box}{\Box}$$

---

3 Make a list of 12 different toppings you could put on a pizza. Circle $\frac{1}{6}$ of the toppings. Draw stars above $\frac{2}{3}$ of the toppings. Make check marks next to $\frac{1}{4}$ of the toppings. Then draw a smiley face next to your favorite topping.

---

4 How can the fractions $\frac{5}{12}$ and $\frac{7}{12}$ be used to describe the letters in the word *denominators*? Explain. Then write two fractions that describe the letters in each word below.

fraction
numerator
part
whole

---

5 Do the practice page "It's a Toss Up!"

---

6 Copy and then fill in the boxes with different fractions that make each statement true.

A. $\frac{1}{5} < \frac{\Box}{\Box} < \frac{3}{5}$

B. $\frac{1}{3} < \frac{\Box}{\Box} < \frac{2}{3}$

C. $\frac{1}{2} < \frac{\Box}{\Box} < \frac{3}{4}$

D. $\frac{3}{8} < \frac{\Box}{\Box} < \frac{7}{8}$

E. $\frac{1}{4} < \frac{\Box}{\Box} < \frac{5}{6}$

---

7 Draw a picture that illustrates each item below.

A. $\frac{3}{4}$ of 20

B. $\frac{2}{3}$ of 12

C. $\frac{3}{5}$ of 10

D. $\frac{5}{6}$ of 18

---

8 Which of the fractions below are equivalent fractions? How do you know?

$\frac{3}{4}$ $\frac{6}{10}$ $\frac{5}{6}$

$\frac{3}{5}$ $\frac{2}{3}$

---

9 Write each fraction in simplest form. Then arrange the fractions from least to greatest.

$\frac{4}{20}$ $\frac{3}{5}$ $\frac{3}{9}$

$\frac{2}{4}$ $\frac{10}{12}$ $\frac{9}{12}$

$\frac{4}{6}$ $\frac{5}{20}$ $\frac{10}{25}$

Note to the teacher: Program the student directions with the number of activities to be completed. Then copy the page and page 24 (back-to-back if desired) for each student.

23

Fraction Basics

Name _____   Date _____

It's a Toss Up!

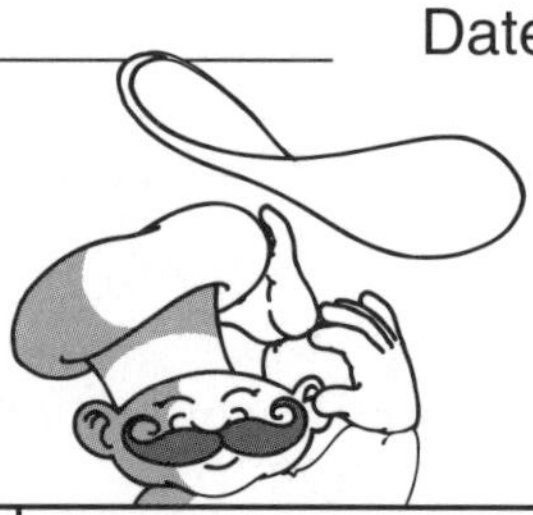

Circle the largest fraction in each set.
Draw a box around the smallest fraction.

$\frac{2}{4}$	$\frac{5}{6}$	$\frac{1}{6}$	$\frac{1}{2}$	$\frac{3}{8}$	$\frac{5}{8}$	$\frac{1}{2}$	$\frac{3}{4}$	$\frac{1}{4}$	$\frac{1}{2}$	$\frac{1}{3}$	$\frac{1}{4}$
H	(F)	[D]	G	K	L	U	E	A	I	O	U
$\frac{1}{10}$	$\frac{3}{5}$	$\frac{7}{10}$	$\frac{1}{10}$	$\frac{1}{2}$	$\frac{2}{5}$	$\frac{11}{12}$	$\frac{3}{4}$	$\frac{7}{12}$	$\frac{3}{8}$	$\frac{1}{4}$	$\frac{5}{8}$
B	D	H	M	P	F	N	O	A	T	S	E
$\frac{1}{6}$	$\frac{1}{3}$	$\frac{5}{12}$	$\frac{3}{5}$	$\frac{7}{10}$	$\frac{9}{10}$	$\frac{1}{4}$	$\frac{1}{12}$	$\frac{1}{6}$	$\frac{1}{2}$	$\frac{1}{5}$	$\frac{3}{10}$
E	O	I	G	L	K	Y	O	A	W	Y	E
$\frac{5}{6}$	$\frac{2}{3}$	$\frac{1}{12}$	$\frac{4}{5}$	$\frac{3}{10}$	$\frac{9}{10}$						
D	K	M	A	I	U						
$\frac{7}{8}$	$\frac{5}{6}$	$\frac{11}{12}$	$\frac{1}{8}$	$\frac{1}{4}$	$\frac{3}{4}$						
M	L	G	F	D	H						
$\frac{5}{12}$	$\frac{2}{3}$	$\frac{5}{6}$	$\frac{1}{3}$	$\frac{7}{8}$	$\frac{1}{2}$						
U	E	O	B	C	H						

Why did Barry decide to go into the pizza business?

To find out, write the letters from the unmarked fractions in reverse order on the lines.

He heard

___ ___   ___   ___ ___ ___ ___ ,

___   ___ ___ ___ ___

___ ___ ___ ___ ___ ___ !

Fraction Basics

Name _____

Date _____

Choose ____ or more activities to do.
When you finish an activity, color its number.

1 Write ten different fractions that would have four as a denominator when written in simplest form. $\dfrac{1}{4}$ $\dfrac{3}{4}$	**2** Match each set of numbers to its greatest common factor (GCF). **A.** 30, 48, 60 $GCF = 4$ **B.** 48, 108, 84 $GCF = 6$ **C.** 36, 68, 96 $GCF = 8$ **D.** 32, 104, 80 $GCF = 12$	**3** All of the Green Sox baseball players' uniforms have prime numbers. List five or more numbers between 20 and 50 that are prime. 
4 Name two numbers that can be substituted for *n* in each statement. **A.** $\dfrac{1}{n} > \dfrac{1}{5}$ **C.** $\dfrac{2}{n} > \dfrac{1}{5}$ **B.** $\dfrac{1}{n} < \dfrac{1}{5}$ **D.** $\dfrac{2}{n} < \dfrac{1}{5}$	**5** Do the practice page "Hey, Batter!" 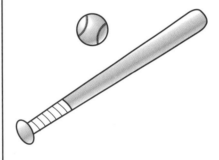	**6** Write each fraction on a different card. Then write the fractions' simplest forms on 12 more cards. Finally, use the cards to play a memory game. $\dfrac{15}{30}$ $\dfrac{12}{32}$ $\dfrac{21}{24}$ $\dfrac{9}{12}$ $\dfrac{33}{55}$ $\dfrac{12}{15}$ $\dfrac{8}{12}$ $\dfrac{25}{100}$ $\dfrac{4}{20}$ $\dfrac{25}{30}$ $\dfrac{6}{18}$ $\dfrac{4}{32}$
7 Draw the caps in order from greatest to least. 	**8** Create a mini poster that explains how to rename an improper fraction as a mixed number. $\dfrac{37}{2} = 18\dfrac{1}{2}$	**9** List the four fractions that are equivalent to $2\dfrac{1}{6}$. Then explain how you identified each one. $\dfrac{6}{13}$ $\dfrac{13}{6}$ $\dfrac{39}{18}$ $\dfrac{26}{12}$ $\dfrac{61}{2}$ $\dfrac{52}{24}$

Note to the teacher: Program the student directions with the number of activities to be completed. Then copy the page and page 26 (back-to-back if desired) for each student.

Fraction Basics

Renaming Fractions as Mixed Numbers

Why are baseball players so rich?

Write each fraction as a whole or mixed number.
To answer the batter's question, write the matching letter from the code below each fraction pair.

Hey, Batter!

Code

$1\frac{5}{6}$ = O
$1\frac{7}{8}$ = Y
2 = A
$2\frac{1}{5}$ = T
$2\frac{1}{3}$ = B
$2\frac{5}{8}$ = D
$2\frac{5}{6}$ = I
$3\frac{1}{2}$ = S
$3\frac{2}{3}$ = L
$3\frac{3}{4}$ = E
$4\frac{1}{6}$ = C
$4\frac{1}{3}$ = M
$4\frac{3}{4}$ = P
$5\frac{1}{3}$ = H
$5\frac{1}{2}$ = U
$5\frac{7}{8}$ = N

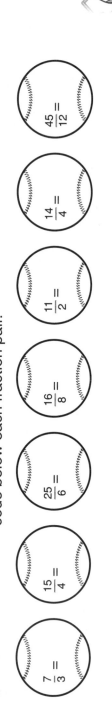

$\frac{7}{3}$ =

$\frac{15}{4}$ =

$\frac{25}{6}$ =

$\frac{16}{8}$ =

$\frac{11}{2}$ =

$\frac{14}{4}$ =

$\frac{45}{12}$ =

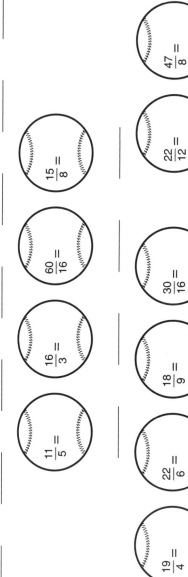

$\frac{21}{8}$ =

$\frac{19}{4}$ =

$\frac{22}{6}$ =

$\frac{11}{5}$ =

$\frac{16}{3}$ =

$\frac{60}{16}$ =

$\frac{15}{8}$ =

$\frac{18}{9}$ =

$\frac{30}{16}$ =

$\frac{22}{12}$ =

$\frac{47}{8}$ =

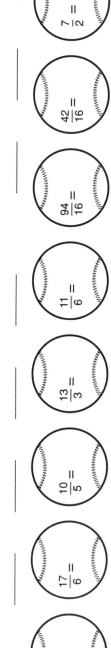

$\frac{17}{6}$ =

$\frac{10}{5}$ =

$\frac{13}{3}$ =

$\frac{11}{6}$ =

$\frac{94}{16}$ =

$\frac{42}{16}$ =

$\frac{7}{2}$ =

Note to the teacher: Use with page 25.

Fractions
Addition and Subtraction, Like Denominators

Name _____

Date _____

Choose ___ or more activities to do.
When you finish an activity, color its number.

---

1 Draw a number line for each problem. Then solve the problem and write the sum in its simplest form.

Example: $\frac{1}{4} + \frac{3}{4} = \frac{4}{4}$, or 1

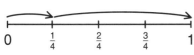

A. $\frac{1}{4} + \frac{1}{4}$ C. $\frac{1}{3} + \frac{1}{3}$

B. $\frac{1}{8} + \frac{5}{8}$ D. $\frac{1}{6} + \frac{4}{6}$

---

2 Spin the spinner twice to name two fractions. Write and solve an addition problem using the fractions. Then simplify the sum. Repeat ten times.

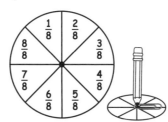

---

3 Write three different addition problems that equal $2\frac{11}{12}$. Then write three different subtraction problems that equal $\frac{3}{8}$.

$$x + y = 2\frac{11}{12}$$
$$x - y = \frac{3}{8}$$

---

4 Write a word problem to match each equation. Then find the answers.

A. $\frac{2}{5} + \frac{4}{5} = n$

B. $2 - \frac{3}{8} = n$

C. $3\frac{3}{4} - \left(\frac{3}{4} + \frac{1}{4}\right) = n$

---

5 Do the practice page "Making the Grade."

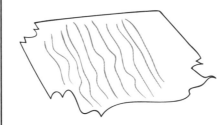

---

6 Create a mini poster that explains how to subtract mixed numbers that have the same denominators.

denominator

whole number

subtract

numerator

simplest form

difference

---

7 Use the mixed numbers to write and solve five different subtraction problems. Then write each difference in its simplest form.

$3\frac{2}{10}$ $4\frac{1}{10}$ $1\frac{6}{10}$

$5\frac{4}{10}$ $8\frac{7}{10}$ $2\frac{8}{10}$

$9\frac{5}{10}$ $6\frac{3}{10}$ $9\frac{10}{10}$ $7\frac{9}{10}$

---

8 Find two different solutions for the problem using the digits 1, 3, 4, 5, and 7.

$$\frac{\square\frac{\square}{8}}{-\ \square\frac{\square}{8}} $$
$$4\frac{\square}{8}$$

---

9 Check the equations shown. If the sum or difference is incorrect, write the correct answer.

A. $\frac{5}{12} + \frac{3}{12} = \frac{8}{24}$

B. $\frac{82}{100} - \frac{47}{100} = \frac{7}{20}$

C. $10\frac{7}{8} - 6\frac{3}{8} = 4\frac{1}{2}$

D. $3\frac{5}{10} - 2\frac{8}{10} = 1\frac{3}{10}$

E. $5\frac{4}{6} - \frac{1}{6} = 5\frac{1}{2}$

Note to the teacher: Each student needs a paper clip to complete activity 2. Program the student directions with the number of activities to be completed. Then copy the page and page 28 (back-to-back if desired) for each student.

Fractions

Addition and Subtraction, Like Denominators

Name _____

Date _____

Making the Grade

Add or subtract. Write each answer in its simplest form.

(O) $\dfrac{3}{6} + \dfrac{1}{6}$

(W) $\dfrac{1}{3} + \dfrac{2}{3}$

(T) $\dfrac{3}{10} + \dfrac{6}{10}$

(Y) $\dfrac{3}{6} - \dfrac{1}{6}$

(A) $\dfrac{4}{12} + \dfrac{1}{12}$

(I) $\dfrac{4}{5} - \dfrac{2}{5}$

(U) $\dfrac{10}{12} - \dfrac{3}{12}$

(C) $\dfrac{4}{8} + \dfrac{5}{8}$

(V) $\dfrac{6}{6} - \dfrac{1}{6}$

(E) $\dfrac{56}{100} + \dfrac{24}{100}$

(S) $\dfrac{8}{10} + \dfrac{6}{10}$

(L) $\dfrac{3}{4} - \dfrac{1}{4}$

(F) $\dfrac{7}{8} - \dfrac{5}{8}$

(P) $\dfrac{4}{5} - \dfrac{3}{5}$

(R) $\dfrac{2}{3} + \dfrac{2}{3}$

What would you get if you could cross a dog, a cat, and an A+?

To find out, write each letter on its matching line or lines.

"
$\dfrac{5}{12}$ — $\dfrac{1}{5}$ $\dfrac{5}{12}$ 1 $1\dfrac{2}{5}$

$\dfrac{2}{5}$ — $\dfrac{9}{10}$ $\dfrac{2}{5}$ $\dfrac{4}{5}$ $\dfrac{1}{2}$ $\dfrac{1}{3}$

$\dfrac{1}{5}$ — $\dfrac{7}{12}$ $1\dfrac{1}{3}$ $1\dfrac{1}{3}$ $\dfrac{1}{4}$ $\dfrac{4}{5}$ $1\dfrac{1}{8}$ $\dfrac{2}{3}$

"
$1\dfrac{2}{5}$ $1\dfrac{1}{8}$ $1\dfrac{1}{3}$ $\dfrac{4}{5}$ $\dfrac{9}{10}$!

Note to the teacher: Use with page 27.

Adding and Subtracting
Fractions With Unlike Denominators

Name _____

Date _____

Choose ___ or more activities to do.
When you finish an activity, color its number.

---

1 | Fraction A's numerator is 3. Fraction B's denominator is more than 5 but less than 15. Write fractions A and B to correctly complete the equation.

$$\frac{\square}{\square} + \frac{\square}{\square} = 1\frac{1}{5}$$

Fraction   Fraction
  A   B

2 | Follow the directions.

1. Flip a coin six times.
2. Write a fraction that describes the number of times the coin lands on heads.
3. Flip the coin eight times and write a fraction for the number of times the coin lands on heads.
4. Add the fractions.
5. Repeat Steps 1–4, writing fractions for the number of times the coin lands on tails.

3 | Find the value of the symbol in each equation.

A. $\frac{9}{10} - \frac{\stackrel{\star}{}}{5} = \frac{\stackrel{\star}{}}{10}$

B. $\frac{\smiley}{2} - \frac{3}{8} = \frac{\smiley}{8}$

C. $\frac{4}{12} + \frac{@}{6} = \frac{@}{2}$

D. $\frac{\blacktriangle}{12} + \frac{\blacktriangle}{6} = \frac{\blacktriangle}{4}$

---

4 | How would you teach a younger student to solve this problem? Write the steps in order.

$$\frac{3}{4} - \frac{3}{8}$$

5 | Do the practice page "Strike?"

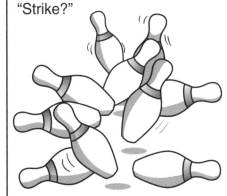

6 | Add each fraction in column B to one of the fractions in column A. Then subtract each fraction in column A from one of the fractions in column B.

A	**B**
$\frac{2}{3}$	$\frac{11}{12}$
$\frac{1}{4}$	$\frac{7}{10}$
$\frac{5}{6}$	$\frac{7}{8}$

---

7 | Solve the problem. Then write another problem like it. (The denominator in the simplified answer will not match either of the denominators in the problem.)

$$\frac{7}{12} - \frac{1}{4}$$

8 | Copy the puzzle. Then add fractions so that when you add two circles on any of the triangle's sides, you get the sum in the square.

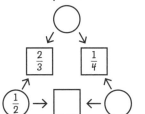

9 | Draw a diagram for each problem. Then solve.

Example: $\frac{1}{4} + \frac{1}{8} = \frac{3}{8}$

A. $\frac{1}{3} + \frac{3}{8}$

B. $\frac{1}{6} + \frac{3}{8}$

C. $\frac{1}{6} + \frac{3}{4}$

Choose & Do Math Grids • ©The Mailbox® Books • TEC61229 • Key p. 91

Note to the teacher: Program the student directions with the number of activities to be completed. Then copy the page and page 30 (back-to-back if desired) for each student.

Name _____   Date _____

Strike?

Solve each problem. Then shade the matching bowling pin.

1. $\frac{7}{10} + \frac{4}{5} =$ _____

2. $\frac{1}{4} + \frac{5}{8} =$ _____

3. $\frac{3}{7} + \frac{1}{3} =$ _____

4. $\frac{3}{4} + \frac{3}{8} =$ _____

5. $\frac{11}{12} - \frac{3}{4} =$ _____

6. $\frac{8}{10} - \frac{2}{5} =$ _____

7. $\frac{4}{5} - \frac{5}{8} =$ _____

8. $\frac{3}{5} - \frac{3}{10} =$ _____

9. $\frac{1}{4} + \frac{1}{2} + \frac{1}{8} =$ _____

10. $\frac{1}{6} + \frac{1}{3} + \frac{5}{8} =$ _____

11. $\frac{4}{9} + \frac{1}{3} + \frac{1}{6} =$ _____

12. $\frac{11}{12} - \frac{7}{8} =$ _____

13. $\frac{9}{10} - \frac{5}{6} =$ _____

14. $\frac{3}{8} + \frac{1}{2} + \frac{3}{4} =$ _____

15. $\frac{5}{6} - \frac{7}{10} =$ _____

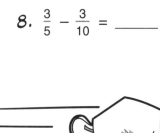

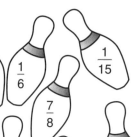
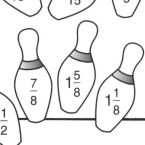

Adding and Subtracting

Mixed Numbers and Fractions With Unlike Denominators

Name _____

Date _____

Choose ___ or more activities to do.
When you finish an activity, color its number.

---

1 Write four mixed numbers using digits from the dates listed. Then add all four mixed numbers. Write the sum in simplest form.

- yesterday's date
- today's date
- tomorrow's date
- your birthdate

September 26, 2012
$9\frac{26}{30}$

2 Copy each pair of problems. Next, circle the problem you think will have the greater difference. Then solve each problem to check your estimate.

A. $2\frac{5}{8} - 1\frac{1}{4}$ **B.** $4\frac{2}{5} - 2\frac{3}{8}$ **C.** $6\frac{1}{4} - 3\frac{1}{8}$

$2\frac{5}{9} - 1\frac{1}{5}$ $4\frac{1}{5} - 2\frac{2}{8}$ $6\frac{1}{5} - 3\frac{1}{7}$

3 The chicken weighs $\frac{3}{4}$ of a pound less than 9 pounds. The rooster weighs $\frac{1}{3}$ of a pound more than 9 pounds. The chick weighs $\frac{1}{2}$ pound. How much do they weigh altogether?

---

4 Add the mixed number in the center to each mixed number around the wheel. You should solve six problems.

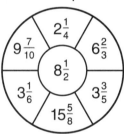

5 Do the practice page "The Chicken Dance?"

CLAP!
CLAP!
CLAP!

6 Copy and complete the chart.

	Add $1\frac{1}{3}$.	Subtract $1\frac{1}{3}$.
$6\frac{1}{5}$		
$4\frac{1}{8}$		
$7\frac{7}{12}$		
$1\frac{5}{6}$		

---

7 For the heads, each square equals 1, each circle equals $\frac{1}{10}$, and each triangle equals $\frac{1}{4}$. Find the sum of the heads. Then create two new heads and use the code to find the sum.

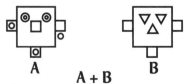

A   B

A + B

8 Solve the riddle. Then write a riddle of your own.

I am a mixed number. When you add me to $1\frac{3}{8}$, you get a sum of $4\frac{3}{5}$. What mixed number am I?

9 Write five different problems, each with a difference of $2\frac{3}{8}$.

$2\frac{3}{8}$

Note to the teacher: Program the student directions with the number of activities to be completed. Then copy the page and page 32 (back-to-back if desired) for each student.

Adding and Subtracting

Mixed Numbers and Fractions With Unlike Denominators

Name _____   Date _____

The Chicken Dance?

Complete the chart. Then use the chart to answer the questions. Write each answer in simplest form.

Dozens of Eggs Laid by Farmer Brown's Hens					
Hen	May	June	July	August	Total
Gladys	2	$2\frac{1}{2}$	$1\frac{1}{3}$	$1\frac{1}{4}$	
Maude	$2\frac{1}{2}$	$2\frac{1}{3}$	$1\frac{3}{4}$	$1\frac{2}{3}$	
Shelly	$1\frac{11}{12}$	$1\frac{3}{4}$	$2\frac{1}{12}$	$1\frac{7}{12}$	
Total					$22\frac{2}{3}$

1. During which month did the hens lay the most eggs?

   _____

2. Which hen laid the most eggs? _____

3. Which hen laid fewer eggs: Shelly or Gladys?
   _____ How many fewer? _____

4. In July, which hen laid more eggs: Maude or Gladys?
   _____ How many more? _____

5. In May, which hen laid more eggs: Gladys or Shelly?
   _____ How many more? _____

6. During which month did the hens lay the fewest eggs?

   _____

7. What is the difference between Shelly's total and Maude's
   total? _____

8. How many dozens of eggs did Gladys and Shelly lay
   altogether? _____

9. During which month did the hens lay more eggs: May or June?
   _____ How many more? _____

10. How many dozen eggs did the hens lay during June, July,
    and August? _____

Workspace

Multiplying Fractions
By Fractions and Whole Numbers

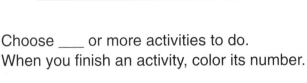

Name _____

Date _____

Choose ___ or more activities to do.
When you finish an activity, color its number.

---

1 Copy and complete the table.

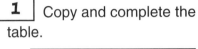

x	2	3	4
$\frac{1}{4}$			
$\frac{1}{2}$			
$\frac{3}{4}$			

---

2 Follow Steps 1–4 for each number shown. Then complete Step 5.

4, 36, 48, 72

1. Add 100.
2. Then multiply by $\frac{1}{4}$.
3. Subtract 25.
4. Multiply by 4.
5. Describe what happens. Why do you think it happens?

---

3 How many pounds (#) are in each box? Which boxes will balance the scale?

$\frac{1}{3}$ of 63#

A. $\frac{5}{8}$ of 24#   C. $\frac{1}{6}$ of 30#

B. $\frac{3}{5}$ of 35#   D. $\frac{3}{4}$ of 28#

---

4 Use the code to solve each problem. Then order the products from least to greatest.

% = 5	@ = 2
& = 7	$ = 4

A. $\frac{@}{\%} \times \frac{@}{\%}$ C. $\frac{\&}{\$} \times \%$

B. $\frac{@}{\&} \times \frac{\$}{@}$ D. $\frac{\%}{\&} \times \frac{\$}{@}$

---

5 Do the practice page "Measure Twice!"

---

6 Write a fraction that describes the number of letters in your first name that are vowels. Do the same for your last name and then multiply the fractions. Repeat five times using different names.

Ann $(\frac{1}{3})$ Smith $(\frac{1}{5})$
$\frac{1}{3} \times \frac{1}{5}$

---

7 Use the formula to find the area of each triangle.

area (a) = $\frac{1}{2}$ × base (b) × height (h)

$(a = \frac{1}{2} bh)$

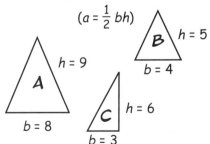

A h = 9 b = 8
B h = 5 b = 4
C h = 6 b = 3

---

8 Create a poster that explains how to find the product.

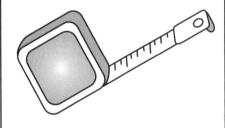

$$\frac{1}{4} \times \frac{3}{4} = n$$

---

9 Solve each problem.

A. There are 88 black and white keys on a piano. Of every 22 keys, nine are black. How many keys are black? How many are white? What fraction describes the number of white keys?

B. Five-twelfths of 24 piano keys are black. How many keys are black? How many are white? What fraction describes the number of white keys?

Choose & Do Math Grids • ©The Mailbox® Books • TEC61229 • Key p. 91

Note to the teacher: Program the student directions with the number of activities to be completed. Then copy the page and page 34 (back-to-back if desired) for each student.

Multiplying Fractions

By Fractions and Whole Numbers

Name ______________________________ Date ____________________

Measure Twice!

Multiply. Write each product in simplest form. Then cross out the matching product.

A. $3 \times \frac{5}{12} =$

B. $\frac{2}{3} \times \frac{6}{8} =$

C. $\frac{6}{8} \times \frac{5}{12} =$

D. $\frac{3}{5} \times 11 =$

E. $7 \times \frac{1}{5} =$

F. $\frac{2}{3} \times \frac{9}{12} =$

G. $6 \times \frac{3}{8} =$

H. $\frac{9}{10} \times \frac{3}{4} =$

I. $\frac{5}{8} \times 4 =$

J. $\frac{6}{12} \times \frac{8}{10} =$

K. $16 \times \frac{1}{4} =$

L. $\frac{5}{6} \times \frac{3}{4} =$

M. $\frac{2}{10} \times \frac{1}{6} =$

N. $\frac{7}{8} \times 9 =$

O. $\frac{4}{5} \times \frac{2}{3} =$

P. $5 \times \frac{7}{12} =$

Q. $\frac{3}{5} \times \frac{7}{12} =$

R. $12 \times \frac{3}{8} =$

S. $7 \times \frac{9}{12} =$

T. $\frac{5}{6} \times \frac{5}{8} =$

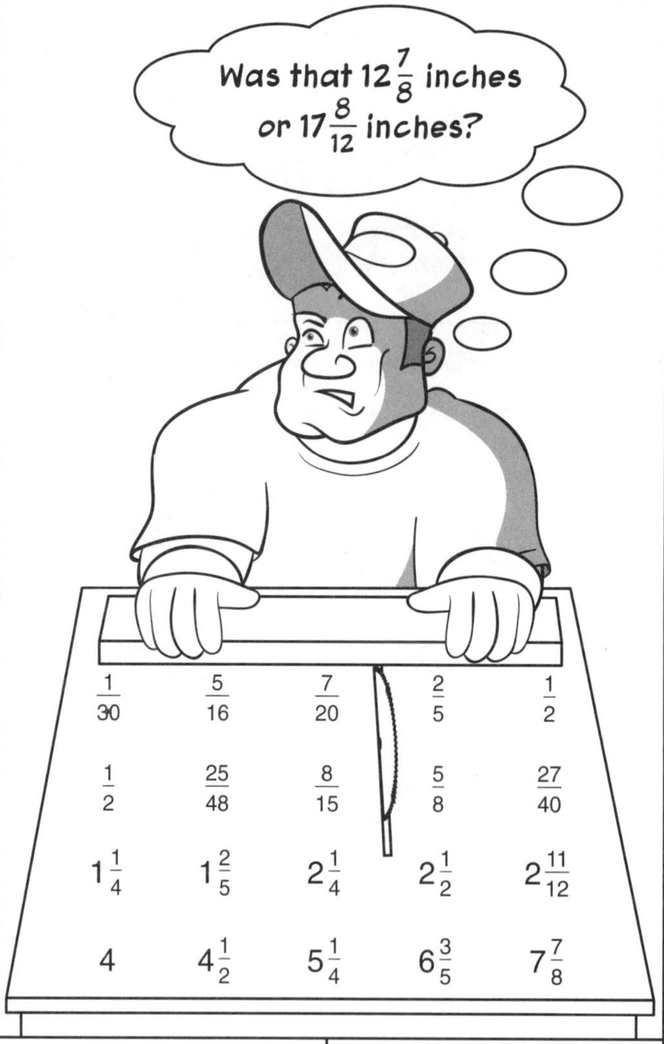

Was that $12\frac{7}{8}$ inches or $17\frac{8}{12}$ inches?
$\frac{1}{30}$ $\frac{5}{16}$ $\frac{7}{20}$ $\frac{2}{5}$ $\frac{1}{2}$
$\frac{1}{2}$ $\frac{25}{48}$ $\frac{8}{15}$ $\frac{5}{8}$ $\frac{27}{40}$
$1\frac{1}{4}$ $1\frac{2}{5}$ $2\frac{1}{4}$ $2\frac{1}{2}$ $2\frac{11}{12}$
4 $4\frac{1}{2}$ $5\frac{1}{4}$ $6\frac{3}{5}$ $7\frac{7}{8}$

 Note to the teacher: Use with page 33.

Multiplying
Mixed Numbers

Name _____

Date _____

Choose ___ or more activities to do.
When you finish an activity, color its number.

---

1 Create and then solve four problems using this format.

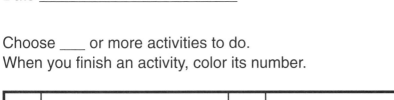

2 To make one quilt, Polly Ester needs the following lengths of fabric:

- $4\frac{7}{8}$ yards purple stripe
- $3\frac{1}{4}$ yards blue dots
- $3\frac{5}{12}$ yards solid green

How many yards of each fabric will she need to make 3, 4, 5, and 6 quilts?

3 For each pair of problems, predict the one that will have the greater product. Then solve each problem to check.

A. $3\frac{1}{2}$ x 2 or $2\frac{1}{2}$ x 3

B. $5\frac{1}{5}$ x 4 or $4\frac{1}{5}$ x 5

C. $4\frac{2}{3}$ x 3 or $3\frac{2}{3}$ x 4

---

4 Use the code to find the product of the values in each color word.

B = $\frac{7}{8}$	I = $\frac{1}{5}$	T = $4\frac{1}{8}$
D = $3\frac{1}{6}$	L = $5\frac{1}{3}$	U = $\frac{1}{6}$
E = $2\frac{1}{3}$	R = $\frac{1}{4}$	W = $\frac{3}{4}$
H = $\frac{5}{6}$		

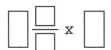

RED   WHITE   BLUE

5 Do the practice page "Looking High and Low."

6 One and a half is half as much as three. So why is $1\frac{1}{2}$ twice as much as $\frac{3}{4}$? Explain with words and a diagram.

---

7 Chairs are worth $1\frac{1}{3}$. Desks are worth $1\frac{2}{5}$. Multiply to find the value of all the chairs in your classroom. Then multiply to find the value of all the desks.

8 Multiply each mixed number in the star by the fraction in the center.

9 Copy and correct each problem.

A. $\frac{3}{4}$ x $4\frac{4}{5}$ = $4\frac{12}{20}$

B. $\frac{5}{8}$ x $5\frac{2}{3}$ = $5\frac{10}{24}$

C. $\frac{7}{12}$ x $3\frac{1}{2}$ = $3\frac{7}{24}$

D. $\frac{1}{6}$ x $6\frac{1}{8}$ = $6\frac{1}{48}$

Choose & Do Math Grids •©The Mailbox® Books • TEC61229 • Key p. 91

Note to the teacher: Program the student directions with the number of activities to be completed. Then copy the page and page 36 (back-to-back if desired) for each student.

Multiplying
Mixed Numbers

Name _____   Date _____

Looking High and Low

Solve. Write each product in simplest form. Show your work.

(E) $3\frac{1}{4} \times 6 =$

(E) $2\frac{5}{8} \times 8 =$

(O) $2\frac{4}{5} \times 5 =$

(S) $3\frac{2}{5} \times \frac{1}{10} =$

(A) $10\frac{1}{2} \times \frac{1}{3} =$

(M) $2\frac{2}{5} \times \frac{3}{4} =$

(H) $7\frac{5}{6} \times \frac{1}{3} =$

(C) $3\frac{1}{8} \times \frac{1}{2} =$

(R) $\frac{2}{3} \times 8\frac{2}{3} =$

(R) $4\frac{3}{5} \times \frac{5}{6} =$

(Y) $8\frac{1}{2} \times \frac{1}{6} =$

(T) $7\frac{3}{5} \times 2\frac{1}{2} =$

(W) $6\frac{1}{4} \times 2\frac{4}{5} =$

(R) $4\frac{7}{10} \times 3\frac{1}{3} =$

(T) $5\frac{1}{8} \times 1\frac{2}{3} =$

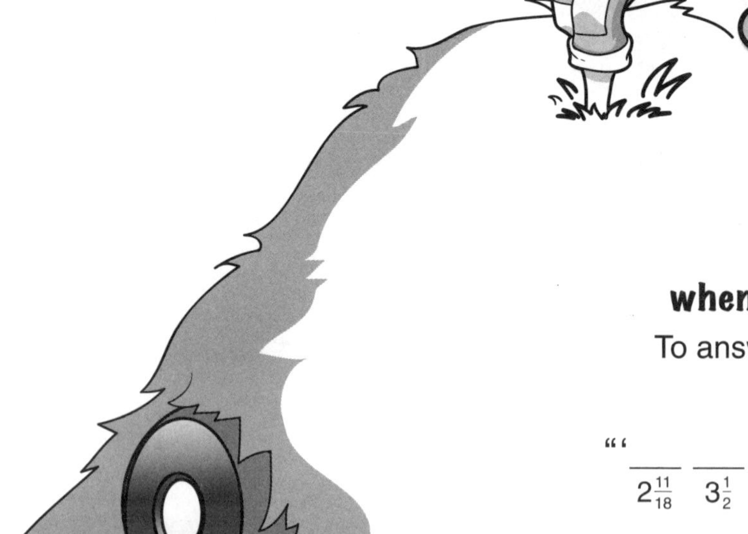

What did the farmer say when she couldn't find her tractor?

To answer the riddle, write each letter on its matching line or lines.

" ‘ ___ ___ ___ , ___ ___ ___ ___ ___ ___ ,
$2\frac{11}{18}$ $3\frac{1}{2}$ $1\frac{5}{12}$ $17\frac{1}{2}$ $2\frac{11}{18}$ $19\frac{1}{2}$ $5\frac{7}{9}$ 21 $\frac{17}{50}$

___ ?"

___ ___ ___ ___ ___ ___ ___ ___
$1\frac{4}{5}$ $1\frac{5}{12}$ $8\frac{13}{24}$ $15\frac{2}{3}$ $3\frac{1}{2}$ $1\frac{9}{16}$ 19 14 $3\frac{5}{6}$

Choose & Do Math Grids • ©The Mailbox® Books • TEC61229 • Key p. 91

Decimal Place Value Through Hundredths

Name _____

Date _____

Choose ____ or more activities to do.
When you finish an activity, color its number.

---

1 Write each number in the format shown. Then write an equivalent fraction or mixed number.

A. 11.09 **D.** 0.50

B. 21.60 **E.** 6.15

C. 0.06 **F.** 7.41

$$8.7 = (8 \times 1) + (7 \times 0.1) = 8\frac{7}{10}$$

---

2 Copy the first number and then flip a coin. If it lands on heads, write the two decimals that come before the number. If it lands on tails, write the two decimals that come after the number. Repeat with each number.

A. 2.5   **E.** 11.8
B. 3.5   **F.** 2.39
C. 4.83 **G.** 9.2
D. 5.06 **H.** 16.4

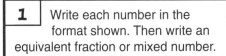

7.4
7.3, 7.2

---

3 Copy the chart. Then complete it by writing each decimal as a fraction or mixed number in simplest form.

Fraction	Decimal
	0.8
	0.12
	0.25
	8.1
	0.15
	.035
	1.47
	0.08
	11.9
	9.4

---

4 Write each fraction on a card. Then convert each fraction to a decimal and write it on the card's flip side. Use the cards as flash cards to help you remember fractions and their decimal equivalents.

$\frac{1}{4}$ $\frac{1}{2}$ $\frac{3}{4}$ $\frac{1}{3}$ $\frac{2}{3}$

$\frac{1}{5}$ $\frac{2}{5}$ $\frac{3}{5}$ $\frac{4}{5}$ $\frac{5}{10}$

---

5 Do the practice page "Time 'Four' a Haircut."

---

6 Write each number in word form. Be sure to write *and* for the decimal point.

2.14

207.05

8,000.8

145.9

63.52

18.95 = eighteen and ninety-five hundredths

---

7 Arrange the decimals in order from greatest to least.

12.9	12.3	12.47	12.05
12.5	12.02	12.1	12.75
12.59	12.6	12.08	12.18
12.04	12.07	12.52	12.17
12.95	12.94	12.99	12.8

---

8 Write the digit 9 and a decimal point. Then roll a die two times and write the numbers to the right of the decimal point. Repeat to make six different decimal numbers. Then compare ten different number pairs using <, >, or =.

9.32 < 9.41

---

9 Copy and complete the chart.

Number	Rounded to the Nearest Whole Number	Rounded to the Nearest Tenth
0.89	1	0.9
1.28		
5.14		
6.39		
4.52		
7.45		
9.61		

Choose & Do Math Grids • ©The Mailbox® Books • TEC61229 • Key p. 91

Note to the teacher: Program the student directions with the number of activities to be completed. Then copy the page and page 38 (back-to-back if desired) for each student.

Name _____   Date _____

Time "Four" a Haircut

Circle the digit 4 in each number. Then shade the box that names its place value.

Just a trim?

A	103.4	tens	ones	tenths
B	47.31	tenths	tens	ones
C	934.2	tens	ones	hundredths
D	7,561.04	hundredths	tenths	hundreds
E	340.5	hundreds	tens	ones
F	64.26	tens	tenths	ones
G	2.47	ones	hundredths	tenths
H	2,783.94	hundreds	tenths	hundredths
I	40.11	ones	tens	tenths
J	745.77	tens	hundreds	ones
K	58.4	tenths	hundredths	tens
L	747.3	ones	tens	hundreds
M	2,496.08	thousands	ones	hundreds
N	19.48	ones	tenths	hundredths
O	3,164.2	tens	ones	thousands
P	405.81	thousands	tens	hundreds
Q	8.49	tens	ones	tenths
R	6,149.25	tenths	tens	hundredths
S	360.42	tenths	ones	tens
T	9.84	hundredths	tenths	tens

To find out which haircut Jake gets, circle the style under the column with the most shaded boxes.

Choose & Do Math Grids • ©The Mailbox® Books • TEC61229 • Key p. 91

Decimal Place Value Through Thousandths

Name _____

Date _____

Choose ___ or more activities to do.
When you finish an activity, color its number.

---

1 Copy each number and then write the value of the digit 1 each time it occurs.

A. 182.371 D. 18,750.019

B. 2,014.913 E. 159.108

C. 491.185 F. 7,163.421

> 18.013: ten, one hundredth

2 Copy and complete each number as guided.

- Make the tenths digit three less than the thousandths digit. Make the hundredths digit two more than the tenths digit.

0.__ __9, 0.__ __4, 0.__ __5

- Make the thousandths digit two more than the tenths digit. Make the hundredths digit one less than the tenths digit.

0.3__ __, 0.1__ __, 0.6__ __

3 Write each decimal in word form and in expanded form.

(A) 12.308

(B) 9.074

(C) 60.152

(D) 200.418

(E) 53.016

---

4 Use the code to write each number.

Code	
○ = one	△ = one tenth
□ = one hundredth	◇ = one thousandth

A. 2.301 D. 0.001

B. 1.022 E. 1.103

C. 3.112 F. 2.033

> 3.123 = ○○○ and △□□◇◇◇

5 Do the practice page "Plop!"

6 Copy each number and then circle a digit as described. Then write the digit's value.

- If the digit in the tenths place is a 1, circle the digit in the thousandths place.

- If the digit in the thousandths place is a 4, circle the digit in the hundredths place.

A. 13.122 E. 4.514

B. 10.974 F. 0.148

C. 1.754 G. 5.161

D. 15.294 H. 6.187

---

7 Make a chart labeled as shown. Then write each number in the correct column.

has three tenths	has six hundredths	has two thousandths

0.063 0.632

36.002 0.326 3.26

2.306

6.032 20.063

62.306

8 Rearrange the digits in each number to make the largest number you can without moving the decimal. Then put your numbers in order from least to greatest.

10.617 52.756

49.315 32.906

74.183 20.379

9 Copy and complete the chart.

Number	+ one tenth	+ one hundredth	+ one thousandth
1.823	1.923	1.833	1.824
6.752			
9.360			
5.148			
3.071			
8.205			

Choose & Do Math Grids • ©The Mailbox® Books • TEC61229 • Key p. 92

Note to the teacher: Program the student directions with the number of activities to be completed. Then copy the page and page 40 (back-to-back if desired) for each student.

39

Name _____   Date _____

Plop!

Write each number.

A. five and three thousandths
_____

B. one hundred twenty-five and one tenth
_____

Pedro's in, and I'm next!

C. three hundred and twenty-one thousandths
_____

D. one and twelve thousandths
_____

E. seventy-eight and two hundredths
_____

F. fourteen and fifty-five hundredths
_____

G. seventeen and nine tenths
_____

H. sixty-four and seven hundredths
_____

I. thirty-one and nine hundredths
_____

J. forty-five and one hundred sixteen thousandths
_____

Write each number in word form.

K. 6.325 _____

L. 204.08 _____

M. 182.407 _____

N. 0.016 _____

Choose & Do Math Grids • ©The Mailbox® Books • TEC61229 • Key p. 92

Addition and Subtraction of Decimals
to Thousandths

Name _____

Date _____

Choose ___ or more activities to do.
When you finish an activity, color its number.

---

1 Use the digits 1–9 to write a problem with a difference that's between 21 and 22. Then solve the problem.

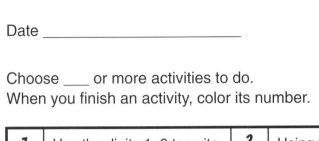

2 Using the numbers below, write five addition and five subtraction problems. Then solve each one.

> 6.8
> 14.271
> 3.49
> 8.053
> 4.95
> 7.09

3 Draw a diagram that shows how to solve each problem. Then solve the problems.

A. $0.8 + 0.8 =$ _____

B. $0.008 + 0.808 =$ _____

C. $0.08 + 0.8 =$ _____

---

4 Using the numbers shown, write and solve a problem that matches each description.

A. has a sum greater than 25
B. has a sum less than 25
C. has a difference less than 2
D. has a difference greater than 2

15.7   11.48   13.55
   6.793   14.208

5 Do the practice page "Buried in Books!"

6 Copy and complete each problem.

A. $24.283 - \Box\Box.\Box\Box\Box = 10.321$

B. $\Box.\Box\Box\Box - 3.572 = 2.752$

C. $81.164 - \Box.2\Box6 = \Box3.\Box78$

D. $\Box6.\Box23 - 11.453 = 15.37\Box$

---

7 Add the number on the left to each number on the right. Then subtract each number on the right from the number on the left.

25.059

22.101
9.08
11.423
0.758

8 Find the missing addend or subtrahend for each problem.

A. $26.148 + 7.327 + \_\_ = 40.138$

B. $\_\_ + 30.743 + 22.681 = 54.388$

C. $19.962 - \_\_ = 12.074$

D. $41.804 + \_\_ + 6.027 = 102.074$

E. $\_\_ - 75.195 = 20.583$

9 Copy the flow chart. Write a starting number in the oval. Then complete the steps shown. What is unusual about the end number? Explain.

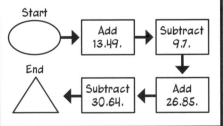

Choose & Do Math Grids • ©The Mailbox® Books • TEC61229 • Key p. 92

Note to the teacher: Program the student directions with the number of activities to be completed. Then copy the page and page 42 (back-to-back if desired) for each student.

41

Addition and Subtraction of Decimals
to Thousandths

Name _____ Date _____

Buried in Books!

Add or subtract. Then shade the matching book below.

1
```
   5.936
+  3.829
```

2
```
  90.62
+ 35.88
```

3
```
  45.81
- 17.35
```

4
```
   2.269
-  1.451
```

5
```
  26.351
- 12.523
```

6
```
   3.339
+  2.652
```

7
```
  26.463
-  9.896
```

8
```
   5.689
-  3.295
```

9
```
  18.246
+  9.276
```

10
```
  67.925
- 26.931
```

11
```
  31.284
+  6.174
```

12
```
  18.270
-  7.941
```

13
```
  49.16
- 14.68
```

14
```
   7.453
+  4.842
```

15
```
  31.158
- 29.079
```

16
```
   8.175
+  2.634
```

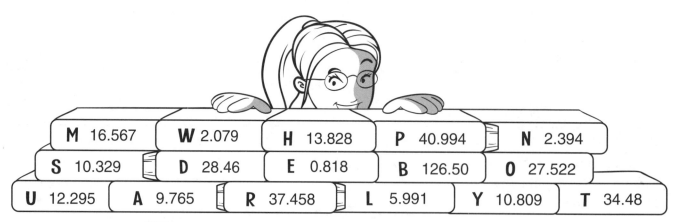

| M 16.567 | W 2.079 | H 13.828 | P 40.994 | N 2.394 |

| S 10.329 | D 28.46 | E 0.818 | B 126.50 | O 27.522 |

| U 12.295 | A 9.765 | R 37.458 | L 5.991 | Y 10.809 | T 34.48 |

What did one math book ask another math book?

To solve the riddle, write the letter from each shaded book
on its matching numbered line or lines.

____ ____   ____ ____ ____   ____ ____ ____ ____   ____ ____
28.46 27.522 10.809 27.522 12.295   2.079 9.765 2.394 34.48   34.48 27.522

____ ____ ____ ____   ____ ____   ____ ____ ____ ____ ____   ____ ____ ____ ?
13.828 0.818 9.765 37.458 16.567 10.809 40.994 37.458 27.522 126.50 5.991 0.818 16.567 10.329

Choose & Do Math Grids • ©The Mailbox® Books • TEC61229 • Key p. 92

Note to the teacher: Use with page 41.

Multiplying Decimals

Name _____

Date _____

Choose ___ or more activities to do.
When you finish an activity, color its number.

---

1 | Use a paper clip and pencil to spin each spinner. Use the numbers to write and then solve a multiplication problem. Repeat ten times.

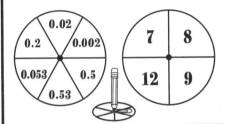

Spinner 1: 0.02, 0.002, 0.5, 0.53, 0.053, 0.2
Spinner 2: 7, 8, 9, 12

---

2 | Estimate to find out which problem matches each description. Then solve each problem to check.

A. The product is less than 100 but greater than 10.

B. The product is less than 1.

C. The product is greater than 100.

D. The product is less than 10 but greater than 1.

0.336 x 3 = n   3.576 x 30 = n

0.395 x 0.3 = n   0.359 x 30 = n

---

3 | Use the code to write and then solve each statement.

● = 1	◇ = 2
△ = 3	■ = 4

A. ●.△ x △.■

B. ■◇.● x ◇●.△

C. ◇△.■ x ●◇.△

D. ●◇■.△ x △.◇

---

4 | Write and solve five different multiplication problems using the numbers below.

1.8   2.4   0.08
0.012
0.005
3.6   0.081
0.45
0.121   0.48

---

5 | Do the practice page "On the Clock."

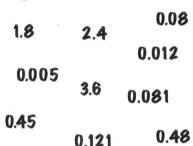

---

6 | Multiply. Then write >, <, or = in each circle.

A. 0.6 x 0.5 ◯ 0.006 x 0.5

B. 4.08 x 0.3 ◯ .408 x 3.0

C. 10.2 x 0.15 ◯ 5.1 x 0.3

D. 0.09 x 9.1 ◯ 2.07 x 0.3

---

7 | Find the value of each symbol. Create a code and then rewrite each equation.

Ⓐ 0.6 x 0.6 = ☆.◎ ✿

Ⓑ 12.1 x 0.5 = ✿.☆ ☽

Ⓒ 5 x 6.1 = ◎ ☆.☽

Ⓓ 3.1 x 0.02 = ☆.☆ ✿ #

Ⓔ 7.25 x 5 = ◎ ✿.# ☽

---

8 | If you were to teach a younger student how to solve the problem shown, what would be the most important thing you would tell her? Explain.

4.9 x 11.13 = n

---

9 | What is wrong with this problem? Explain and then solve it correctly.

$$
\begin{array}{r}
1.4 \\
\times\ 3.9 \\
\hline
12.6 \\
4.2 \\
\hline
16.8
\end{array}
$$

Note to the teacher: Give students access to a paper clip to complete activity 1. Program the student directions with the number of activities to be completed. Then copy the page and page 44 (back-to-back if desired) for each student.

Multiplying Decimals

Name _____   Date _____

On the Clock

Multiply.
Shade the box with the matching answer.

A   3.7
    x 1.5

B   25
    x 6.4

C   0.8
    x 7.3

D   0.7
    x 0.6

E   11.9
    x 0.6

F   2.34
    x 5.9

G   19.8
    x 0.05

H   7.89
    x 3.6

I   79.1
    x 6.3

J   0.456
    x   7

K   8.99
    x 41.7

L   602.7
    x 0.3

0.990	an
13.806	her
498.33	help
0.41	a
28.404	Get
5.55	for
374.883	the
0.42	him
3.182	Give
5.84	its
7.24	hand
160.0	Go
3.192	helping
7.14	Grab
180.81	head
5.74	it

If your clock can't tell time, what should you do?
To solve the riddle, unscramble the unshaded words on the clock.
Then write the words in order on the lines.

_____ _____ _____ _____!

Choose & Do Math Grids •©The Mailbox® Books • TEC61229 • Key p. 92

44   **Note to the teacher:** Use with page 43.

Dividing Decimals

Name _____

Date _____

Choose ____ or more activities to do.
When you finish an activity, color its number.

---

1 Solve each problem. Then write the quotients from greatest to least.

A. $3\overline{)97.2}$ **D.** $5\overline{)42.5}$

B. $7\overline{)6.37}$ **E.** $8\overline{)208.4}$

C. $6\overline{)124.2}$ **F.** $4\overline{)54.08}$

____, ____, ____, ____, ____, ____
greatest   least

---

2 Find the matching divisor and quotient for each problem. Then write the complete equation.

A. $\overline{)83.7}$ 6) $\overline{)}^{\,8.37}$

B. $\overline{)49.05}$ 5) $\overline{)}^{\,9.81}$

C. $\overline{)26.73}$ 9) $\overline{)}^{\,9.3}$

D. $\overline{)50.22}$ 3) $\overline{)}^{\,8.91}$

---

3 Write a division problem for each description below. Use 5 as the divisor in every problem.

The quotient is _____.

A. less than 1

B. greater than 11 but less than 12

C. greater than 25 but less than 26

D. greater than 50 but less than 51

A. $5\overline{)1.5}^{\,0.3}$

---

4 Use the divisors and dividends to write and solve five division problems.

Divisors	Dividends
2	439.2 14.4
4	8.04
6	340.56 70.8
8	389.4

---

5 Do the practice page "A Sweet Treat."

---

6 For each problem, find the divisor (other than 1) that results in the greatest possible quotient. Repeat, finding the divisor for each problem that results in the least possible quotient.

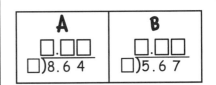

A	**B**
□.□□	□.□□
□)8.6 4	□)5.6 7

---

7 Find four incorrect problems. Rewrite each one correctly.

A. $5.44 \div 4 = 1.036$

B. $129.5 \div 5 = 25.9$

C. $31.86 \div 9 = 3.54$

D. $78.6 \div 6 = 1.31$

E. $149.6 \div 2 = 7.406$

F. $14.84 \div 7 = 20.12$

---

8 Explain how to find the unit price, the cost of one item, in each set. Then find each unit price.

6-pack of soda $2.58

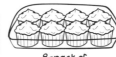
8-pack of cupcakes $6.24

4-pack of juice boxes $3.84

Chocolate Bar
2-pack of candy bars $1.96

---

9 Divide each number on the wheel by the number in the center.

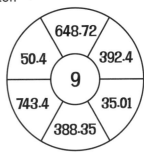

648.72
50.4
392.4
9
743.4
35.01
388.35

Note to the teacher: Program the student directions with the number of activities to be completed. Then copy the page and page 46 (back-to-back if desired) for each student.

45

Dividing Decimals

Name _____   Date _____

A Sweet Treat

Divide. Circle the letter in the column that best describes the quotient. Show your work.

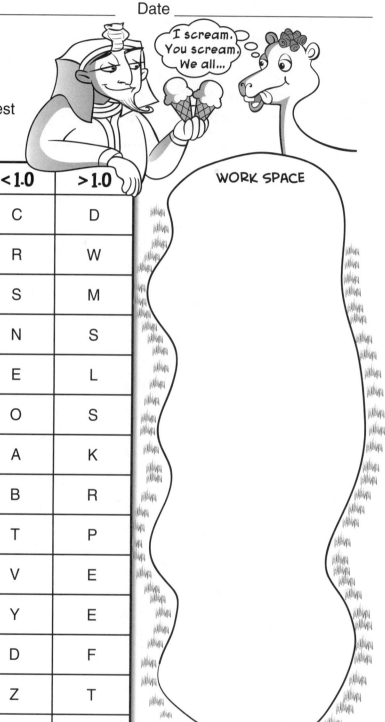

I scream. You scream. We all...

WORK SPACE

		< 1.0	> 1.0
1	$95.9 \div 7 =$	C	D
2	$5.034 \div 6 =$	R	W
3	$1.392 \div 4 =$	S	M
4	$275.2 \div 8 =$	N	S
5	$0.711 \div 9 =$	E	L
6	$35.8 \div 2 =$	O	S
7	$0.042 \div 3 =$	A	K
8	$314.5 \div 5 =$	B	R
9	$6.792 \div 8 =$	T	P
10	$203.6 \div 4 =$	V	E
11	$99.42 \div 6 =$	Y	E
12	$0.301 \div 7 =$	D	F
13	$411.5 \div 5 =$	Z	T
14	$2.124 \div 9 =$	E	X

What would you call ice cream for a camel?

To answer the riddle, write each circled letter on its matching numbered line.

____ ____ ____ ____ ____ ____ ____   ____ ____ ____ ____ ____ ____ ____ !
0.014 0.043 16.57 0.348 0.079 62.9 0.849   13.7 0.236 34.4 17.9 50.9 0.839 82.3

Choose & Do Math Grids • ©The Mailbox® Books • TEC61229 • Key p. 92

Fractions as Ratios

Name _____

Date _____

Choose ___ or more activities to do.
When you finish an activity, color its number.

---

1 For each fraction, write three equal ratios.

$\frac{1}{2}$ $\frac{5}{8}$

$\frac{3}{5}$

$\frac{15}{20}$ $\frac{4}{7}$

$\frac{2}{3}$ = 4 to 6 = 8:12 = $\frac{10}{15}$

---

2 If the ratios are equal, write =.
If they are not equal, write ≠.

Example: $\frac{3}{10}$ ≠ $\frac{9}{10}$

A. $\frac{18}{3}$ ☐ $\frac{48}{8}$

B. $\frac{35}{5}$ ☐ $\frac{28}{7}$

C. $\frac{72}{9}$ ☐ $\frac{64}{8}$

D. $\frac{60}{10}$ ☐ $\frac{18}{2}$

E. $\frac{32}{4}$ ☐ $\frac{56}{8}$

---

3 Use the data to write five different ratio statements.

Tank 1	16 🐠	8 🐡	Total 24
Tank 2	12 🐠	14 🐡	Total 26

The ratio of 🐠 in Tank 1 to the total number of fish in the tank is 16:24.

---

4 Write each fraction as a ratio. Then draw a picture and write a statement that explains the ratio.

A. $\frac{4}{5}$ C. $\frac{3}{4}$

B. $\frac{5}{8}$ D. $\frac{6}{10}$

$\frac{1}{2}$ = 1:2, or 1 white fish to 2 striped fish

---

5 Do the practice page "Under the Sea."

---

6 Draw a picture for each ratio that shows whether each pair of ratios is equal. Then complete each statement with = or ≠.

A. $\frac{1}{3}$ ◯ 3:9

B. $\frac{2}{6}$ ◯ 1:3

C. $\frac{3}{4}$ ◯ 4:8

---

7 Write each ratio as a fraction in its simplest form.

A. 12:48
B. 18:54
C. 24:60
D. 15:45
E. 21:63

15:30 = $\frac{15}{30}$ = $\frac{1}{2}$

---

8 Write three ratio statements that compare each shape to the other shapes shown.

The ratio of the square to all the shapes is 1:10.

---

9 Write five ratios that compare students in your class.

The number of girls wearing sneakers to the number of boys wearing sneakers is 8 to 12 or $\frac{8}{12}$.

Choose & Do Math Grids • ©The Mailbox® Books • TEC61229 • Key p. 92

Note to the teacher: Program the student directions with the number of activities to be completed. Then copy the page and page 48 (back-to-back if desired) for each student.

47

Fractions as Ratios

Name _____ Date _____

Under the Sea

Color the fish yellow if the fraction and ratio are equal.
Color the fish red if the fraction and ratio are not equal.

A. $9:20 = \frac{45}{100}$

B. $1:4 = \frac{2}{10}$

C. $\frac{16}{50} = 8:25$

D. $7:12 = \frac{15}{24}$

E. $9:5 = \frac{180}{100}$

F. $\frac{1}{2} = 6:13$

G. $2:5 = \frac{40}{100}$

H. $5:6 = \frac{24}{30}$

I. $\frac{11}{25} = 44:100$

J. $3:4 = \frac{75}{100}$

K. $\frac{3}{10} = 6:21$

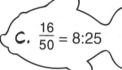

Holy mackerel! This is one smart school of fish!

L. $4:5 = \frac{40}{50}$

M. $\frac{8}{21} = 8:12$

N. $\frac{170}{100} = 17:10$

O. $3:25 = \frac{6}{100}$

P. $\frac{6}{10} = 3:5$

Q. $1:5 = \frac{20}{100}$

R. $\frac{7}{50} = 7:100$

S. $4:7 = \frac{4}{7}$

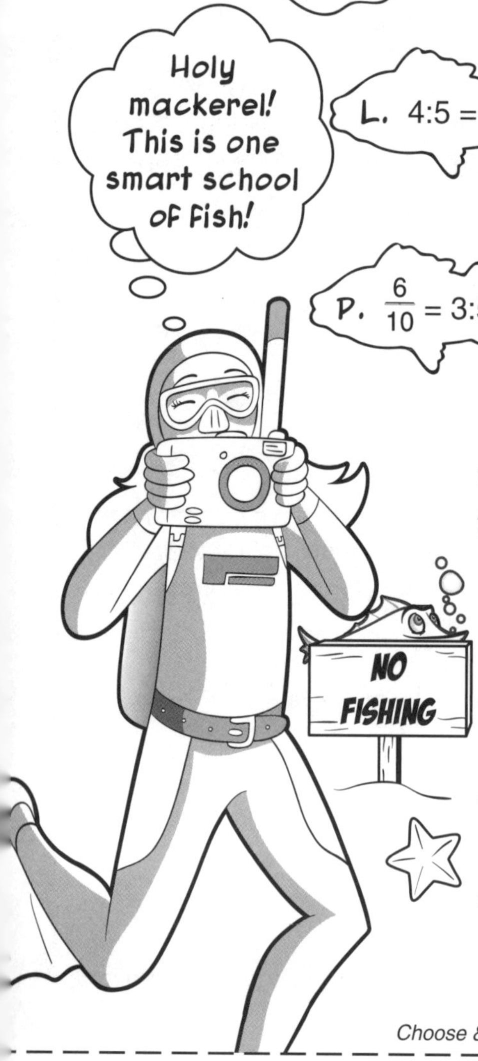

Write the letter of each red fish on a shell. Rewrite the fraction or the ratio to make the pair equal.

NO FISHING

_____   _____

_____   _____

_____   _____

_____   _____

Percents

Name _____

Date _____

Choose ___ or more activities to do.
When you finish an activity, color its number.

| **1** | Write the fraction, decimal, and percent that describe the shaded portion of each figure. |

A.

B.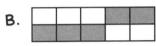

C.

| **2** | A piggy bank has $1.00 in coins. Write the fraction, decimal, and percent that describe each coin or set of coins compared to the amount of money in the bank. |

Example: 1 nickel = $\frac{5}{100}$ = 0.05 = 5%

A. 1 quarter   **C.** 4 nickels
B. 15 pennies   **D.** 4 dimes

| **3** | Copy and complete the chart. |

fraction	equivalent fraction	decimal	percent
$\frac{1}{4}$	$\frac{25}{100}$	0.25	25%
$\frac{2}{25}$			
$\frac{3}{20}$			
$\frac{3}{5}$			
$\frac{1}{2}$			
$\frac{2}{50}$			

| **4** | Draw a 5 x 5 grid. Color the squares as guided. Then write the fraction, decimal, and percent that describe each color's portion of the grid. |

- Color 3 □s red.
- Color 4 □s yellow.
- Color 5 □s orange.
- Color 6 □s green.
- Color 7 □s blue.

| **5** | Do the practice page "Clip and Save." |

| **6** | Write five steps that explain how to find the decimal and fraction that are equal to 35%. |

35%

| **7** | Max has a box of 100 dog treats in a variety of flavors: 10 beef, 20 turkey, 30 chicken, and 40 bacon. Draw a bar graph that shows the percentage of each flavor. |

| **8** | Write a fraction, a decimal, and a percent that describe the shaded parts of each circle. Repeat for the unshaded parts of each circle. |

Example:
 shaded: $\frac{1}{4}$, 0.25, 25%
unshaded: $\frac{3}{4}$, 0.75, 75%

A.   **B.**

| **9** | Create a mini poster that explains how to find the decimal and percent equivalents for $\frac{7}{10}$. |

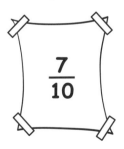

$\frac{7}{10}$

Note to the teacher: Program the student directions with the number of activities to be completed. Then copy the page and page 50 (back-to-back if desired) for each student.

Percents

Name _____   Date _____

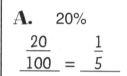

Clip and Save

Convert each percent to a fraction.
Then write each fraction in simplest form.

A. 20% $\frac{20}{100} = \frac{1}{5}$	**B.** 62% ___ = ___

C. 8% ___ = ___	**D.** 35% ___ = ___

E. 58% ___ = ___	**F.** 90% ___ = ___

G. 26% ___ = ___	**H.** 12% ___ = ___

I. 40% ___ = ___	**J.** 88% ___ = ___

K. 65% ___ = ___	**L.** 4% ___ = ___

M. 10% ___ = ___

N. 22% ___ = ___

O. 54% ___ = ___

P. 75% ___ = ___

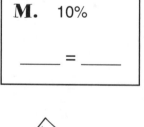
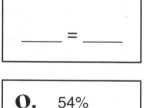

These scissors really help me cut costs!

Choose & Do Math Grids • ©The Mailbox® Books • TEC61229 • Key p. 92

Perimeter

Name _____

Date _____

Choose ___ or more activities to do.
When you finish an activity, color its number.

| **1** Find three objects that have rectangular faces. Draw a model of each object. Next, measure the sides of one rectangular face on each object and label your model. Then calculate each rectangle's perimeter. | **2** Arrange five index cards to make a polygon that has six or more sides. Measure each of the polygon's sides. Then draw the polygon you created, label your drawing, and calculate the shape's perimeter. 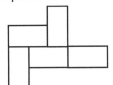 | **3** Roll a pair of dice. Then draw a rectangle using one of the numbers you rolled for its length and the other number for its width. Find the rectangle's perimeter. Repeat the steps four times. |

| **4** Using a ruler, draw four different shapes that each have a perimeter of 48 cm.   | **5** Do the practice page "Paint by Perimeter!" | **6** Write a song or rhyme to help you remember how to find the perimeter (*p*) of a polygon, triangle, quadrilateral, or square.

p of a polygon = the sum of all the sides
p of a triangle = side + side + side
p of a quadrilateral = $2 \cdot$ length $+ 2 \cdot$ width
p of a square = $4 \cdot$ side |

| **7** Copy the chart. Then find the missing measurements to complete it. | **8** For each polygon, find the missing side measurement. Then explain how you found each one.  | **9** Choose three of the careers below. For each one, describe two ways being able to find perimeter would be important.

house painting
architecture
interior decorating
landscaping
farming   **bricklaying** |

Chart for Activity 7:

length	width	perimeter
36 ft.		180 ft.
	25 in.	132 in.
65 cm		260 cm
	72 m	288 m
112 ft.		360 ft.

Note to the teacher: Each student needs five index cards to complete activity 2 and a pair of dice to complete activity 3. Program the student directions with the number of activities to be completed. Then copy the page and page 52 (back-to-back if desired) for each student.

Name _____ Date _____

Paint by Perimeter!

Find each figure's perimeter. Write it on the matching line.
Next, complete the code with your favorite colors. Then color by the code.

A. <u>15 ft.</u>

B. _____

C. _____

D. _____

E. _____

F. _____

G. _____

H. _____

I. _____

J. _____

K. _____

L. _____

M. _____

N. _____

O. _____

P. _____

Q. _____

R. _____

S. _____

T. _____

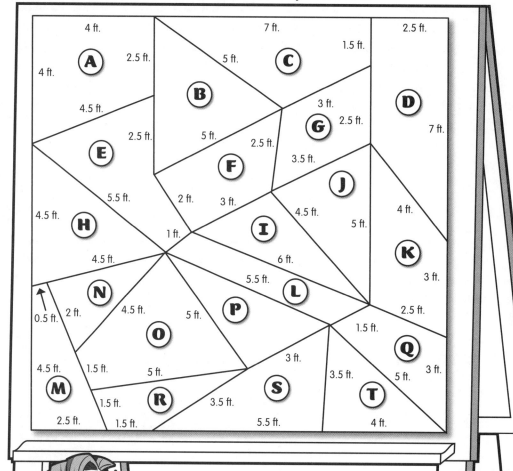

Now this is a masterpiece beyond measure!

PERIMETER COLOR CODE

10–12 ft. = _____   12.5–14 ft. = _____

14.5–15 ft. = _____   15.5–19 ft. = _____

Area and Perimeter

Name _____

Date _____

Choose ___ or more activities to do.
When you finish an activity, color its number.

---

1 Draw eight different rectangles that have perimeters of 36 units.

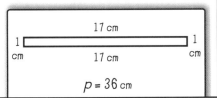

17 cm

1 cm | | 1 cm

17 cm

$p = 36$ cm

---

2 Find the perimeter of the polygon shown. How did you find it? What is the polygon's area? How are they different?

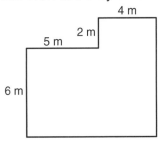

4 m

2 m

5 m

6 m

---

3 Find the area of each rectangle. Which two have a combined total area of 1,000 sq. ft.?

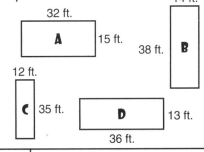

32 ft.

A | 15 ft.

14 ft.

38 ft. | B

12 ft.

C | 35 ft.

D | 13 ft.

36 ft.

---

4 A picture frame's outer dimensions are 16" x 24". The frame is 3" wide all the way around. What are the dimensions, perimeter, and area of the opening for the picture? How did you find your answers?

24"

3"

16"

---

5 Do the practice page "Squeaky Clean."

---

6 Three rectangles have the perimeters listed below. Two of them also have area measurements of 48 cm². Which rectangle cannot have an area measurement of 48 cm²? How do you know?

• Rectangle A's perimeter = 28 cm

• Rectangle B's perimeter = 46 cm

• Rectangle C's perimeter = 32 cm

---

7 Draw a three-column chart. Then sort the area measurements to tell whether they would be, could be, or could not be a square.

49 UNITS²   36 UNITS²   144 UNITS²

25 UNITS²   121 UNITS²   27 UNITS²

54 UNITS²   81 UNITS²   100 UNITS²

42 UNITS²

Would Be a Square	Could Be a Square	Could Not Be a Square

---

8 Choose one of your textbooks and write its title. Next, measure the length and width of the book's front cover and its spine. Calculate the perimeter and area of each one. Then find the total perimeter and area of the book's front cover, spine, and back cover. Repeat with a different textbook.

MATH

---

9 Copy and then complete the chart.

Rectangle Measurements			
Length	Width	Perimeter	Area
9	7	32	63
	6		42
5		20	
	8		48
10		30	
	9		27

Choose & Do Math Grids • ©The Mailbox® Books • TEC61229 • Key p. 93

Note to the teacher: Program the student directions with the number of activities to be completed. Then copy the page and page 54 (back-to-back if desired) for each student.

53

Area and Perimeter

Name _____   Date _____

Squeaky Clean

Find each shape's area and perimeter.

Remember, to find perimeter, add all the sides. To find area, multiply length times width.

A.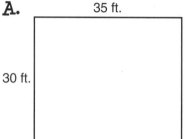
35 ft. / 30 ft.

p = _____

a = _____

B.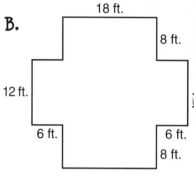
18 ft., 8 ft., 12 ft., 6 ft., 6 ft., 8 ft.

p = _____

a = _____

C.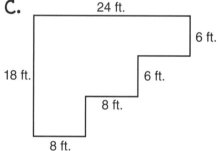
24 ft., 6 ft., 18 ft., 6 ft., 8 ft., 8 ft.

p = _____

a = _____

D.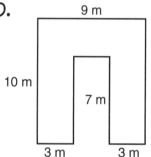
9 m, 10 m, 7 m, 3 m, 3 m

p = _____

a = _____

E.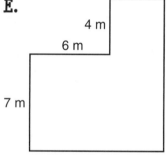
4 m, 4 m, 6 m, 7 m

p = _____

a = _____

F.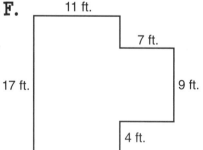
11 ft., 7 ft., 17 ft., 9 ft., 4 ft.

p = _____

a = _____

G.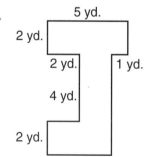
5 yd., 2 yd., 2 yd., 1 yd., 4 yd., 2 yd.

p = _____

a = _____

H.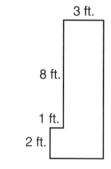
3 ft., 8 ft., 1 ft., 2 ft.

p = _____

a = _____

Customary Measurement

Name _____

Date _____

Choose ___ or more activities to do.
When you finish an activity, color its number.

| 1 | Copy and then complete the capacity chart. |

cups	pints	quarts	gallons
16	8	4	1
			6
	16		
			8

| 2 | Copy and then write <, >, or = to compare the length, capacity, and weight measurements. |

A. 28 inches _____ 1 yard

B. 4 pints _____ 2 quarts

C. 5 pounds _____ 80 ounces

D. 12 yards _____ 56 feet

E. 12 gallons _____ 48 quarts

| 3 | Explain how to convert the measurements below. |

- **15 feet to yards**
- **6 gallons to quarts**
- **3 yards to inches**

To convert 80 ounces to pounds, divide the number of ounces by 16.
80 ounces = 5 pounds

| 4 | Arrange the measurements from heaviest to lightest. |

2 POUNDS
3 POUNDS
40 OUNCES
160 OUNCES
15 POUNDS
320 OUNCES
56 OUNCES
120 POUNDS

| 5 | Do the practice page "A Clean Sweep." |

| 6 | Copy and then complete each analogy. |

A. 12 inches are to 1 foot as 16 ounces are to 1 pound

B. ___ quarts are to 1 gallon as 3 feet are to 1 yard

C. 36 inches are to 1 yard as ___ cups are to 1 gallon

D. gallons are to a bathtub as ___ are to a glass

E. length is to feet as ___ is to pounds

| 7 | Copy and solve each problem. |

A. 1 gallon + 3 quarts = ___ pints

B. 8 pounds + 6 ounces = ___ ounces

C. 16 pints + 16 cups = ___ gallons

D. 2 yards + 18 inches = ___ feet

E. 48 inches + 6 feet = ___ yards

| 8 | Choose five units of measure. For each one, name three objects you could measure using that unit. |

foot

inch   yard

pound

ounce   cup

quart

pint   gallon

| 9 | Fold a sheet of paper twice to make four sections. Cut the sections apart and stack and staple them to make a booklet. Make the first page your cover. On the other pages, show how to convert units of length, weight, and capacity from larger to smaller units. |

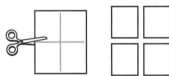

Customary Measurement: Weight

Name _____   Date _____

A Clean Sweep

Shade the box with the most reasonable estimate for each object.
Follow the path of shaded boxes to find out which object Stuart's mom lets him keep.

1.	football helmet	1 oz.	1 lb.	1 T
2.	T-shirt	10 oz.	10 lb.	10 T
3.	pillow	22 oz.	22 lb.	2 T
4.	toy car	6 oz.	6 lb.	6 T
5.	shoebox	8 oz.	8 lb.	8 T
6.	television	43 oz.	43 lb.	43 T
7.	adult male	$\frac{1}{10}$ oz.	$\frac{1}{10}$ lb.	$\frac{1}{10}$ T
8.	basket of toys	4 oz.	4 lb.	4 T
9.	tractor trailer	16 oz.	16 lb.	16 T
10.	box of books	15 oz.	15 lb.	15 T
11.	foam ball	3 oz.	3 lb.	3 T
12.	action figure	5 oz.	5 lb.	5 T
13.	box of crayons	2 oz.	2 lb.	2 T
14.	bowling ball	8 oz.	8 lb.	8 T
15.	horse	$\frac{3}{4}$ oz.	$\frac{3}{4}$ lb.	$\frac{3}{4}$ T
16.	electric guitar	7 oz.	7 lb.	7 T
17.	pair of sunglasses	3 oz.	3 lb.	3 T
18.	baseball bat	32 oz.	32 lb.	32 T

16 ounces (oz.) = 1 pound (lb.)
2,000 pounds (lb.) = 1 ton (T)

I'm sorry; your room is not considered an endangered habitat!

Metric Measurement

Choose ___ or more activities to do.
When you finish an activity, color its number.

---

1 | Arrange the linear measurements from shortest to longest.

92.5 millimeters   7.5 centimeters

95 centimeters   90 centimeters

5 millimeters   1,010 millimeters

4 centimeters   65 millimeters

1 meter   1.1 meters

---

2 | Name the unit in the list below that does not belong. Then explain why.

> meter
> kilometer
> liter
> millimeter
> centimeter

---

3 | Copy and then complete the chart.

> 10 millimeters (mm) = 1 centimeter (cm)
> 100 centimeters (cm) = 1 meter (m)

mm	cm	m
1,000	100	
	250	
		0.5
		12

---

4 | Draw a Venn diagram like the one shown. Then write each item in the appropriate section.

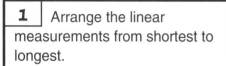

milliliter (mL)   liter (L)

cup of coffee   medicine

soda for 1 person   juice for 1 person

milk for a family   juice for 4 people   water in a bathtub

milk for 1 school lunch

soda for a party   water in a disposable bottle

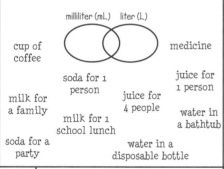

---

5 | Do the practice page "'Four-k' Lift."

---

6 | Tell how many milligrams (mg), grams (g), or kilograms (kg) need to be added to keep each scale balanced.

25 g   mg   **A**

4 kg   g   **B**

3,700 g   kg   **C**

mg   215 g   **D**

0.5 kg   mg   **E**

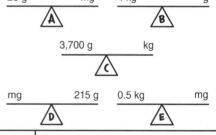

---

7 | Name something that would most likely be measured in each of the units shown.

> millimeters
> kilograms
> centimeters
> grams
> meters
> kilometers

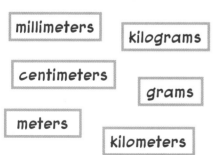

---

8 | Measure eight different line segments on the diagram in centimeters. Then convert each length to millimeters.

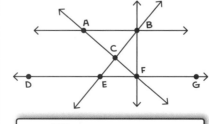

$\overline{AB}$ = 1.5 cm = 15 mm

---

9 | Rewrite each statement, correcting the unit of measure. Then write two statements about yourself that include metric units of measure.

A. A medicine cup holds about five grams.

B. My palm is about 80 centimeters wide.

C. My dad is exactly two millimeters tall.

D. My bathtub holds about 285 kilograms of water.

E. Susan's puppy's mass is less than two liters.

Choose & Do Math Grids • ©The Mailbox® Books • TEC61229 • Key p. 93

Note to the teacher: Program the student directions with the number of activities to be completed. Then copy the page and page 58 (back-to-back if desired) for each student.

57

Metric Measurement

"Four-k" Lift

Measure the length of each fork to the nearest centimeter (cm).
Measure the length of each knife to the nearest millimeter (mm).
Then arrange the measurements from shortest to longest.

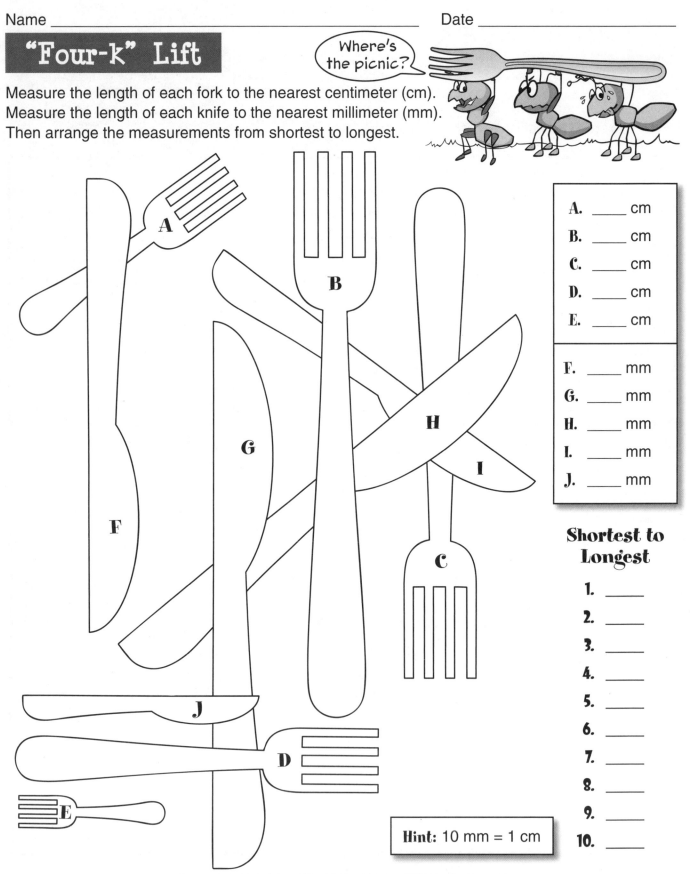

Where's the picnic?

| A. _____ cm |
| B. _____ cm |
| C. _____ cm |
| D. _____ cm |
| E. _____ cm |

| F. _____ mm |
| G. _____ mm |
| H. _____ mm |
| I. _____ mm |
| J. _____ mm |

Shortest to Longest

1. _____
2. _____
3. _____
4. _____
5. _____
6. _____
7. _____
8. _____
9. _____
10. _____

Hint: 10 mm = 1 cm

Choose & Do Math Grids • ©The Mailbox® Books • TEC61229 • Key p. 93

Temperature and Elapsed Time

Name _____

Date _____

Choose ___ or more activities to do.
When you finish an activity, color its number.

---

1 Write each day's temperature in Fahrenheit and Celsius. Then name two outdoor activities that would be appropriate for each day.

°F °C   °F °C   °F °C
A   B   C

2 Copy the chart. To complete it, write the time 45 minutes before and after each time shown.

Before		After
1:45	2:30	3:15
	5:50	
	12:05	
	11:25	
	6:05	
	3:40	
	1:20	

3 Name the warmer temperature in each pair. Then create a bumper sticker that shows the main difference between Fahrenheit and Celsius temperatures.

A. 30°C, 30°F
B. 40°F, 10°C
C. 0°C, 35°F
D. 110°F, 35°C
E. 10°C, 10°F

---

4 Write five time questions about the schedule. Then answer each one.

Example: Which flight is the shortest?

Departure		Arrival	
New York	6:15 AM	Atlanta	7:46 AM
Atlanta	9:47 AM	Denver	2:03 PM
Atlanta	2:59 PM	Philadelphia	4:20 PM
New York	3:38 PM	Chicago	6:14 PM

5 Do the practice page "Time to Adjust."

6 Create a schedule that shows the exact time for each bulleted portion.

- Carl leaves the theater immediately after the movie ends at 4:25.
- The movie lasts 135 minutes.
- Carl watches previews for 18 minutes before the movie starts.
- It takes Carl 7 minutes to get his movie snacks.
- Carl stands in the ticket line for 15 minutes.
- It takes Carl half an hour to walk to the theater.

Event	Time
Carl leaves home.	―――――

---

7 Draw a thermometer that shows the freezing and boiling points on a Fahrenheit scale. Then draw a thermometer that shows the freezing and boiling points on a Celsius scale.

8 Write a story problem about each item below. Then solve the problems and find the missing times.

A. Start: 11:20 PM
Elapsed time: 4 hours, 35 minutes
End: _____
B. Start: _____
Elapsed time: 1 hour, 28 minutes
End: 4:50 AM
C. Start: 5:12 AM
Elapsed time: 78 minutes
End: _____
D. Start: _____
Elapsed time: 119 minutes
End: 10:05 PM

9 Draw a line graph that illustrates the data shown.

Time	Temperature
7:30 AM	58°F
11:30 AM	66°F
3:30 PM	74°F
7:30 PM	65°F
11:30 PM	60°F
3:30 PM	51°F

Choose & Do Math Grids • ©The Mailbox® Books • TEC61229 • Key p. 93

Note to the teacher: Program the student directions with the number of activities to be completed. Then copy the page and page 60 (back-to-back if desired) for each student.

59

Name _____ Date _____

60

Time to Adjust

Write the elapsed time.

Start Time	End Time	Elapsed Time
10:15 AM	12:05 PM	A. 1 hour, 50 minutes
12:50 PM	4:02 PM	B.
8:10 PM	10:41 PM	E.
6:45 AM	9:13 AM	F.
1:20 PM	2:45 PM	H.
4:35 PM	6:20 PM	I.
9:05 AM	10:02 AM	L.
11:25 AM	2:13 PM	M.
2:40 PM	3:35 PM	O.
5:10 PM	7:40 PM	R.
2:30 PM	3:13 PM	S.
10:45 AM	12:25 PM	T.
3:50 PM	6:01 PM	V.
7:25 AM	7:54 AM	X.
1:05	3:15 PM	Y.

WORKSPACE

WHY ARE YOGA INSTRUCTORS SO EASY TO GET ALONG WITH?

To solve the riddle, write each letter on its matching numbered line or lines.

A
___   ___   ___   ___   ___   ___   ___
1 h 40 m 1 h 25 m 2 h 31 m 2 h 10 m   1 h 50 m 2 h 30 m 2 h 31 m

___   ___   ___   ___
2 h 11 m 2 h 31 m 2 h 30 m 2 h 10 m

___   ___   ___   ___   ___   ___
2 h 28 m 57 m 2 h 31 m 29 m   1 h 45 m 3 h 12 m   57 m 2 h 31 m

Note to the teacher: Use with page 59.

Identifying Plane and Solid Figures

Name _____

Date _____

Choose ___ or more activities to do.
When you finish an activity, color its number.

1 Draw a "geom-e-tree." Label the tree trunk "Plane Figures." Draw five or more branches on the tree. Then label each branch with the name of a different plane figure. On each branch, draw four or more leaves and write a different attribute of the figure on each one. *4 right angles*	**2** Cut six same-size paper triangles. On each one, draw a different solid figure and label it and its base, vertices, edges, and faces. Then staple your triangles together to create a banner. *cone* *cube* *cylinder*	**3** Use a ruler to draw a net for each figure. A. triangular prism B. cylinder C. rectangular pyramid D. rectangular prism *cube*
4 Cut out 20 examples of solid figures from old magazines or newspapers. Sort them into four categories according to their attributes. Then glue each category of shapes to a different piece of paper and describe the category on the paper's flip side.	**5** Do the practice page "Up Close!"	**6** Make a list of two or more real-world examples of each figure. **triangular pyramid** **triangle** **triangular prism** **cone** **square pyramid**
7 Describe the plane figure or figures that make up the faces of each solid figure. A. cube B. cylinder C. rectangular pyramid D. rectangular prism E. triangular prism	**8** Research the state flags of the United States. Choose ten flags that each have at least one plane figure. Write the name of each state and describe the geometric figures on each flag.	**9** Use the vertices to name each edge and face of Figures 1 and 2. **Figure 1** **Figure 2** Figure 1 Edge: HI Face: HIJ

Choose & Do Math Grids • ©The Mailbox® Books • TEC61229 • Key p. 94

Note to the teacher: Program the student directions with the number of activities to be completed. Then copy the page and page 62 (back-to-back if desired) for each student.

Identifying Plane and Solid Figures

Name _____ Date _____

Up Close!

Name each figure.
Write your answer in the puzzle.
Then write each circled letter on its
matching numbered line or lines to
complete the statement.

Without ___ ___ ___ ___ ___ ___ ___ ___ ,
         12 5 4 9 5 15 8 16

___ ___ ___ ___ would be
9 10 15 3

" ___ ___ ___ ___ ___ - ___ ___ ___ ___ !"
 11 4 6 7 15   2 5 14 13

Word Bank

circle	hexagon	prism	sphere
cone	octagon	pyramid	square
cube	parallelogram	rectangle	trapezoid
cylinder	pentagon	rhombus	triangle

Choose & Do Math Grids • ©The Mailbox® Books • TEC61229 • Key p. 94

62 **Note to the teacher:** Use with page 61.

Working With Plane Figures

Name _____

Date _____

Choose ___ or more activities to do.
When you finish an activity, color its number.

---

1 The United States flag does not have a line of symmetry. Design three different flags as guided.

A. has one line of vertical symmetry
B. has one line of horizontal symmetry
C. has two lines of symmetry: one vertical and one horizontal

2 Name the triangles that are similar and the triangles that are congruent. Then explain your choices.

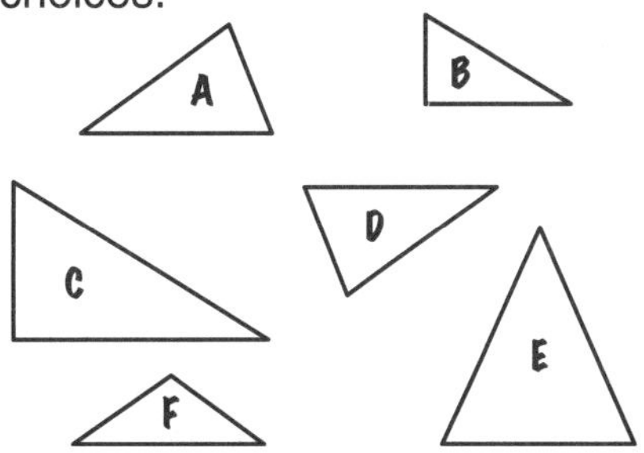

3 Tell whether each letter has vertical, horizontal, or no lines of symmetry. Then draw the letters and add their lines of symmetry.

TRAPEZOID

4 Tell how many lines of symmetry there are in a regular hexagon and in a regular octagon. Explain your answers. Then draw the lines of symmetry to check.

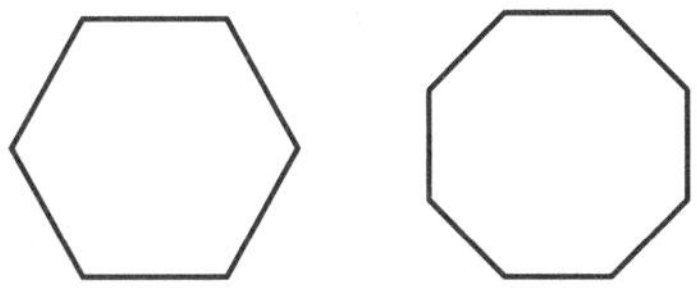

5 Do the practice page "Down by the Seashore."

6 Find two objects that are similar polygons. Name the objects and describe the similarity. Then find three or more different pairs.

My book and our classroom door are similar rectangles.

7 Describe the transformation (*translation, rotation,* or *reflection*) of each figure below.

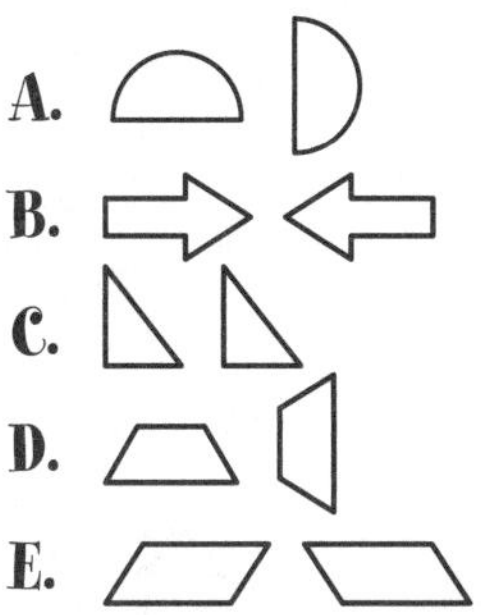

A.
B.
C.
D.
E.

8 Draw a triangle. Then draw its reflection. Next, draw the triangle at a 90° rotation. Repeat with a pentagon and then a shape of your choice.

9 Connect the points on the grid to make five different polygons. Then write each figure's line segments to name it.
Example: $\overline{LW}$, $\overline{SW}$, $\overline{SL}$ = right triangle

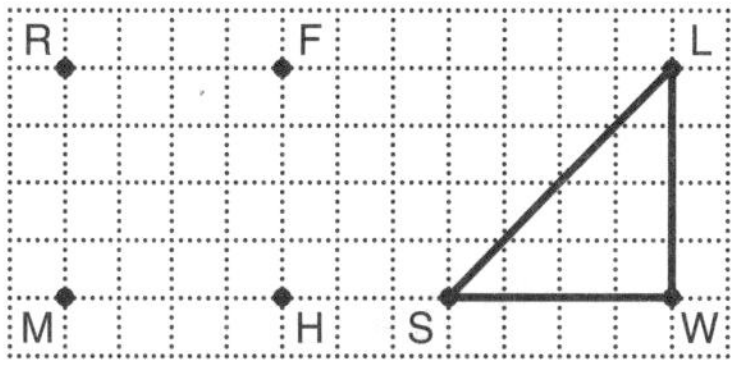

Choose & Do Math Grids • ©The Mailbox® Books • TEC61229 • Key p. 94

Note to the teacher: Program the student directions with the number of activities to be completed. Then copy the page and page 64 (back-to-back if desired) for each student.

63

Date _____

Working With Plane Figures

Down by the Seashore

On each figure, draw all the lines of symmetry.
Then color the shape by the code.

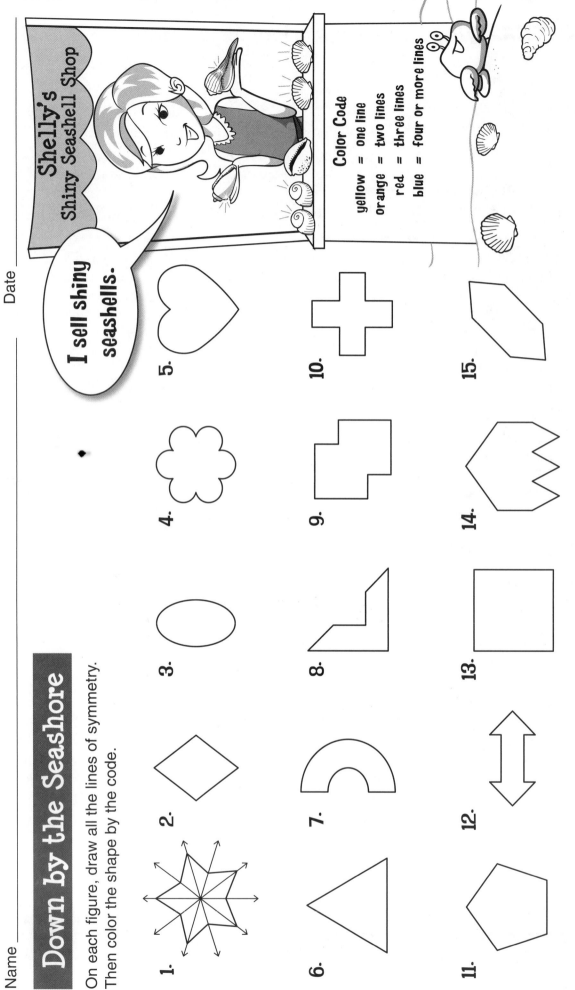

Shelly's
Shiny Seashell Shop

I sell shiny seashells.

Color Code

yellow = one line
orange = two lines
red = three lines
blue = four or more lines

1.

2.

3.

4.

5.

6.

7.

8.

9.

10.

11.

12.

13.

14.

15.

Choose & Do Math Grids • ©The Mailbox® Books • TEC61229 • Key p. 94

Note to the teacher: Use with page 63.

Lines and Line Segments

Name _____

Date _____

Choose ___ or more activities to do.
When you finish an activity, color its number.

---

1 | Using the figure shown, name the parallel, perpendicular, and intersecting line segments.

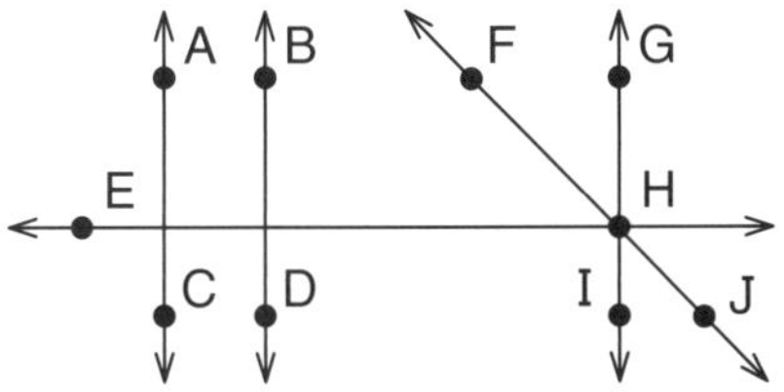

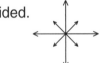

2 | Find and describe two real-world examples each of parallel, perpendicular, and intersecting lines.

3 | Use a ruler to draw a city map with four roads that are parallel to each other, two roads that intersect other roads but are not perpendicular, and four roads that are perpendicular to other roads. Then color the roads according to the code.

> **Road Code**
> blue = parallel
> green = intersecting
> red = perpendicular

---

4 | These two sets of perpendicular lines intersect at one point. Make three drawings as guided.

A. One line intersects three parallel lines.
B. Two pairs of parallel lines form four pairs of perpendicular lines.
C. One pair of parallel lines intersects another pair of parallel lines.

5 | Do the practice page "Street Smart."

6 | Label a three-circle Venn diagram as shown. Then sort the polygons listed below onto the diagram.

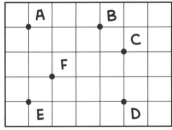

hexagon
octagon
pentagon
rectangle
square
trapezoid
right triangle

---

7 | Use the terms *parallel*, *perpendicular*, and *intersecting* to describe the line segments in each letter.

> F Z I Y
> T H M V L
> W X A
> N

8 | Copy and complete each sentence. Then draw a picture about each sentence.

A. The yard lines on a football field are ___ to each other.
B. Two roads that cross each other at right angles are ___ to each other.
C. The line connecting two bases on a baseball field is a ___.
D. The threads on a spider's web ___ each other.

9 | Connect the points to draw five or more line segments. Then name all the parallel, perpendicular, and intersecting lines.

Note to the teacher: Program the student directions with the number of activities to be completed. Then copy the page and page 66 (back-to-back if desired) for each student.

Lines and Line Segments

Name _____ Date _____

Street Smart

- Use the map to answer the questions.

1. Which road is parallel to Highland Avenue?
   _____

2. Which road is perpendicular to Chase Road?
   _____

3. Which roads intersect Birch Street but are not perpendicular to it? _____
   _____

4. Which two roads are perpendicular to Memorial Highway? _____
   _____

5. Which road intersects but is not perpendicular to Chase Road?
   _____

6. Which road is parallel to Main Street?
   _____

7. Is Hillside Drive parallel to Chase Road? _____
   How do you know? _____
   _____

8. Which roads does Avenue C intersect? _____
   _____
   _____

- Follow the directions.

9. Draw a road west of Memorial Highway that is parallel to the highway. Then name the streets that are perpendicular to it.

10. Draw a road perpendicular to Highland Avenue that intersects Chase Road and Memorial Highway. Then name the streets that are parallel to it.

11. Draw a road from Chase Road that intersects Hillside Drive. Can this road be parallel to another road on the map? _____ Explain. _____
    _____

12. Draw a new road that intersects two or more streets on the map. Name your road and then use *perpendicular, parallel,* and *intersect* to describe each intersection. _____
    _____

Choose & Do Math Grids • ©The Mailbox® Books • TEC61229 • Key p. 94

Triangles and Quadrilaterals

Name _____

Date _____

Choose ___ or more activities to do.
When you finish an activity, color its number.

1 Use a ruler to draw a right, an isosceles, and an equilateral triangle that each have a perimeter of 9 inches. Then label each triangle.	**2** Use the words *sometimes*, *always*, and *never* to write eight sentences that describe triangles. A right triangle always has one 90° angle.	**3** Draw and then name a polygon to match each description. A. two sets of parallel sides, no right angles B. three sides of equal length, three 60° angles C. quadrilateral, one set of parallel sides D. three sides, one 90° angle E. four sides of equal length, all right angles
4 Find objects with the quadrilateral shapes below. List the objects on a chart like the one shown. 	square	rectangle	rhombus	trapezoid
	flag				**5** Do the practice page "High Fiber Diet."	**6** Create a poster about the different types of triangles. right obtuse equilateral isosceles scalene
7 Rewrite each false statement to make it true. A. All of a trapezoid's sides are parallel. B. A square has four acute angles. C. A rhombus is a triangle with opposite sides that are not equal lengths. D. A trapezoid is a parallelogram with four right angles.	**8** Explain why a triangle can have two acute angles but cannot have two right angles or two obtuse angles. Draw diagrams that prove your explanation. 	**9** Cut apart a piece of paper to make four right triangles. Label each right angle. Then use all four triangles to make each shape below. Draw and label a picture of each shape. A. **parallelogram** B. **rectangle** C. **right triangle** square

Note to the teacher: Program the student directions with the number of activities to be completed. Then copy the page and page 68 (back-to-back if desired) for each student.

Triangles and Quadrilaterals

Name _____ Date _____

High Fiber Diet

• Write the word that matches each description.
  Then cross out the word in the word bank.

1. triangle in which all angles measure less than 90°

   __ ◯ __ __ __

2. quadrilateral that has exactly one pair of parallel sides

   __ __ ◯ __ __ __ __ __ __

3. rectangle with four sides of the same length

   __ __ __ __ ◯ __

4. quadrilateral with four right angles and two pairs of congruent sides

   __ __ __ __ __ __ ◯ __

5. triangle with two sides of equal length

   __ __ ◯ __ __ __ __ __ __

6. parallelogram with four congruent sides

   __ ◯ __ __ __ __ __

7. triangle with three sides of equal length

   __ __ __ ◯ __ __ __ __ __ __ __

8. triangle with three sides of unequal lengths

   __ __ __ __ ◯ __ __

9. term that applies to a certain polygon and squares, rectangles, and rhombuses

   __ __ __ __ __ __ __ __ __ __ __ __ ◯

10. triangle with one angle that is greater than 90°

    __ __ ◯ __ __ __

Word Bank

acute	parallel	scalene
angle	parallelogram	square
equilateral	quadrilateral	trapezoid
isosceles	rectangle	triangle
obtuse	rhombus	

Why don't giraffes make good pets?

To answer the riddle, write each circled letter on its matching numbered line or lines.

They ___ ___ E
     2   3

___ ___ ___ ___ ___ ___ ___
10   5   5   6   7   4   6

___ ___ ___ ___ ___ E -
 9   2   7   8   10

___ ___ ___ ___ E!
 8   2   8   1

• Circle the words in the word bank that you did not cross out. Then write a sentence that describes each term.

11. _____   13. _____

    _____   _____

12. _____   14. _____

    _____   _____

Patterns

Name _____

Date _____

Choose ___ or more activities to do.
When you finish an activity, color its number.

---

1 Flight A leaves the runway at 7:07. Flight B leaves at 7:12, flight C departs at 7:18, and flight D exits the runway at 7:25. According to this pattern, what time will flight E leave? Flight F? Flight I? Explain how you know.

2 If you were to complete the code shown using the same pattern, what would letters *H*, *P*, and *W* each equal?

Code

$A = 2$

$B = 4$

$C = 6$

3 Copy each pattern. Find and cross out the mistake in each one. Then write or draw the correct symbol, letter, or number above each mistake.

A. ⊠ ⊠ ⊠ ⊠ ⊠ ⊠

B. AB, FG, LM, SR, UV, YZ

C. 5, 15, 25, 30, 45, 55

D. ♫♫ ♪♪ ♪ ♩ ♫♫ ♪♪ ♪

4 Use symbols like the ones shown to create three different patterns. Show five steps in each pattern and then write each rule.

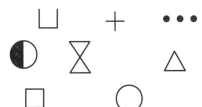

5 Do the practice page "Music to Your Ears?"

6 What will the 15th letter in this pattern be? Show how you know.

a, c, d, f, g, h, j, k, l, m, o,

7 Prudence puts pennies in her bank every day. Judging by this pattern, how many pennies will Prudence put in her bank on Saturday? How much money will she save in all?

Day	Number of Pennies
Sunday	15
Monday	30
Tuesday	60

8 Josh wants to beat his sister's score of 95,000 on Super Spy Spotter. In his first game, Josh scores 5,275 points. In the second game Josh doubles his score. If Josh continues to double his score each game, how many games will he need to play to beat his sister's high score? Explain.

9 Sarah is using the following running schedule to train for soccer. On which day will Sarah start running 5 miles? How many total miles will Sarah be running on the 20th day?

Day 1: $\frac{1}{2}$ mile

Day 2: 1 mile

Day 3: rest

Day 4: $1\frac{1}{2}$ miles

Choose & Do Math Grids • ©The Mailbox® Books • TEC61229 • Key p. 95

Note to the teacher: Program the student directions with the number of activities to be completed. Then copy the page and page 70 (back-to-back if desired) for each student.

Name _____ Date _____

Music to Your Ears?

Write the missing number or draw the missing shape
to complete each pattern. Then write the rule.

E. △ □ □ ○ △ □ □ ____
_____

K. 6, 13, 20, 27, ____
_____

T. 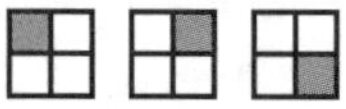 ⊞ ⊞ ⊟ ____
_____

A. ○ ▭ ○○ ▯ ○○○ ____
_____

Y. 2, 3, 5, 8, 12, ____
_____

I. 11, 22, 44, 77, ____
_____

H.  ᄱ ᄱ ᄱ ____
_____

M. 96, ____, 24, 12
_____

C.  ⊠ ⊠ ____ ⊠ ⊠
_____

O. 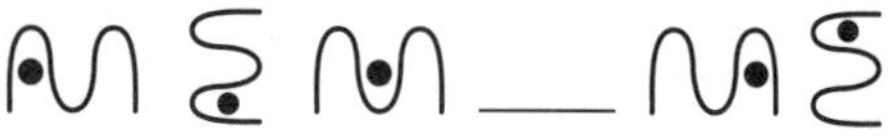 ᄱ ᄝ ᄱ ____ ᄱᄝ
_____

U. 27, 32, 30, 35, ____, 38
_____

S. □ \ □ □ □ ____ □ \ □ □ × □ \
_____

D. 16, 19, 25, 34, ____, 61
_____

P.  / ∧ /\/ ____ /\/ /\/\
_____

**What kind of music would
a bunch of balloons make?**
To find out, write each letter
on the line or lines with the
matching shape or number.

⊟ ᄱ ○ 17 46 ,

48 ▭ 34 ○

" ᄱ ᄝ ᄱ "

48 33 × 121 ⊠ !

Patterns

Name _____

Date _____

Choose ___ or more activities to do.
When you finish an activity, color its number.

| 1 | Arrange the numbers to make a pattern. Describe the pattern and then add four more numbers that continue the pattern.

100.0   101.1

97.8

102.2   98.9 | 2 | It takes four toothpicks to make one square and seven toothpicks to make two squares. How many toothpicks would you need to make eight squares in a row? Draw a diagram to help you.

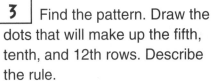 | 3 | Find the pattern. Draw the dots that will make up the fifth, tenth, and 12th rows. Describe the rule.

 |

| 4 | A marching band forms ten rows on the football field. There are four musicians in the first row. Each row has four more musicians than the row before it. How many band members are on the field? How do you know?

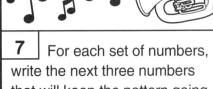 | 5 | Do the practice page "Single File."

 | 6 | Jake walks three-tenths of a mile in four minutes. Then he runs one-half of a mile in two minutes. If Jake repeats this walking and then running pattern for 30 minutes, how many miles will he cover? If Jake continues the pattern for 16 more minutes, how many miles will he cover in all? |

| 7 | For each set of numbers, write the next three numbers that will keep the pattern going. Then write another group of numbers that follows a similar pattern.

A. 100, 97.5, 95, 92.5, 90, __, __, __

B. 3, 9, 36, 180, __, __, __

C. 1, 2.5, 5, 8.5, 13, __, __, __ | 8 | Which two sets of numbers have errors in their patterns? How do you know? How would you correct each one?

A. 13.5, 11.5, 16, 14, 17.5, 15.5

B. 7, 5.5, 8.5, 7, 10, 8.5, 11.5

C. 12, 60, 6, 30, 3, 15, 45

D. 24, 4, 36, 6, 54, 6, 81 | 9 | Write a number pattern of six numbers that follows the rule shown.

Rule: Add $\frac{1}{2}$. Subtract $\frac{1}{4}$.

Example: $3, 3\frac{1}{2}, 3\frac{1}{4},$ |

Note to the teacher: Program the student directions with the number of activities to be completed. Then copy the page and page 72 (back-to-back if desired) for each student.

Name _____   Date _____

Single File

Complete each pattern. Then use a ruler to draw a line to its rule.

① 10, 19, 28, 37, 46, <u>55</u>, <u>64</u> •

② 4; 12; 36; 108; ___; ___; 2,916 •

③ 96, ___, 24, 12, ___, 3, 1.5 •

④ 13, 15, 14, ___, 15, 17, ___ •

⑤ 7, 14, ___, 34, 37, 74, ___ •

⑥ 100, 85, 95, ___, ___, 75, 85 •

⑦ 75,000; 15,000; ___; 600; ___; 24 •

⑧ 77, ___, 67, 62, 57, 52, ___ •

⑨ 30, 10, 60, 20, 120, ___, ___ •

⑩ 124, 120, 123, 119, 122, ___, ___ •

⑪ 384, 359, ___, 309, ___, 259 •

⑫ 10, 5, ___, 10, 40, ___, 80 •

⑬ 13; 130; 65; ___; 325; 3,250; ___ •

⑭ 99, ___, ___, 99, 101, 100, 102 •

⑮ 48, 16, 21, ___, 12, 4, ___ •

• **A.** Subtract 4 and then add 3.

• **B.** Divide by 3 and then multiply by 6.

• **C.** Multiply by 3.

• **D.** Divide by 5.

• **E.** Multiply by 10 and then divide by 2.

• **F.** Add 2 and then subtract 1.

• **G.** Subtract 25.

• **H.** Subtract 15 and then add 10.

• **I.** Subtract 1 and then add 2.

• **J.** Divide by 2.

• **K.** Add 9.

• **L.** Subtract 5.

• **M.** Divide by 2 and then multiply by 4.

• **N.** Multiply by 2 and then add 3.

• **O.** Divide by 3 and then add 5.

Expressions, Variables

Name _____

Date _____

Choose ___ or more activities to do.
When you finish an activity, color its number.

---

1 Copy the table. Then add four more rows with different values for *b* and solve to complete the table.

b	8*b*
7	56
21	
33	

2 List all the possible whole numbers for *n*. Write your own inequality for *n*.

$$3 \times 4 < n < 5 \times 4$$

3 Use the measurements shown to find the missing length or width.

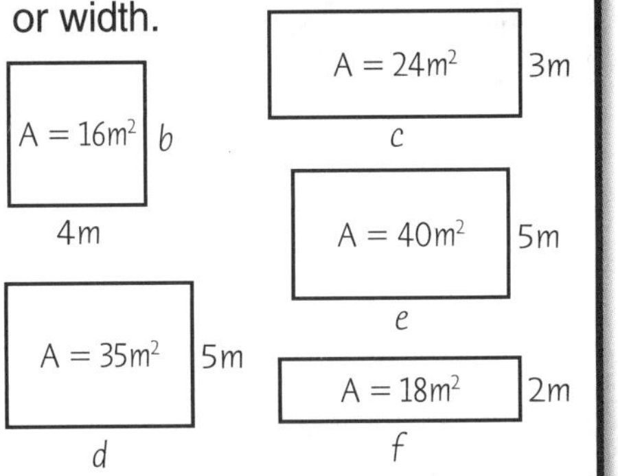

$A = 16m^2$ | *b*
4m

$A = 24m^2$ | 3m
c

$A = 40m^2$ | 5m

$A = 35m^2$ | 5m
d

e

$A = 18m^2$ | 2m
f

---

4 Write four or more steps that explain how to find the value of *b*.

$$45 - (20 \div 4) \times b + 7 = 12$$

5 Do the practice page "Blast Off!"

6 Copy the equations. Then solve for each missing value.

$$17 + r = 16 + 14$$
$$r + 18 = s + 16$$
$$s + r = p + 12$$
$$r + p = s + q$$

$r = \boxed{}$ $s = \boxed{}$
$p = \boxed{}$ $q = \boxed{}$

---

7 Write a word problem for this equation. Draw a picture to illustrate it. Then solve for *n*.

$$30 + 42 + n = 150$$

8 Find the value of *b*. Then copy the diagram and complete it.

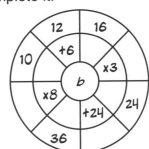

9 Evaluate each expression below for $n = 9$, $n = 15$, and $n = 27$.

A. $7n$

B. $n \times 5 + 6$

C. $25 + n \div 3$

D. $n(75 \div 5)$

Choose & Do Math Grids • ©The Mailbox® Books • TEC61229 • Key p. 95

Note to the teacher: Program the student directions with the number of activities to be completed. Then copy the page and page 74 (back-to-back if desired) for each student.

Name _____   Date _____

Blast Off!

Write the letter of the expression that matches each word phrase.

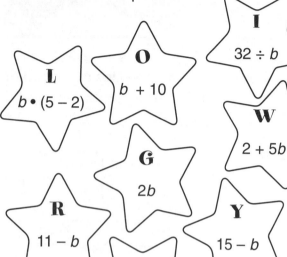

E
1 + b

I
32 ÷ b

O
b + 10

L
b • (5 − 2)

W
2 + 5b

G
2b

R
11 − b

Y
15 − b

F
4b

A
b + (7 + 2)

B
b + 13

H
24 ÷ b

K
b − 2

T
b + 6

V
(6 x 3) − b

_____ **1.** four times as many as b

_____ **2.** ten more than b

_____ **3.** the sum of b and six

_____ **4.** the sum of seven and two plus b

_____ **5.** one increased by b

_____ **6.** 11 decreased by b

_____ **7.** 24 divided by b

_____ **8.** the product of b and the difference between five and two

_____ **9.** the quotient of 32 and b

_____ **10.** 15 decreased by b

_____ **11.** the difference between b and two

_____ **12.** two more than five times b

_____ **13.** b increased by 13

_____ **14.** b less than the product of six and three

_____ **15.** twice as many as b

Why was the astronaut in trouble?

To solve, write each letter on its matching numbered line or lines.

___ ___ ___ ___ ___ ___ ___ ___ ___ ___
7   5   13 6   2   11 5   3   7   5

___ ___ ___ ___ ___ ___ ___ ___ ___ ___ ___ ___ .
8   4   12 2   1   15 6   4   14 9   3   10

Graphs

Name _____

Date _____

Choose ___ or more activities to do.
When you finish an activity, color its number.

---

1 | Write and answer five questions about the line graph.

Weekly Class Averages

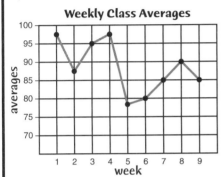

(line graph: y-axis "averages" from 70 to 100, x-axis "week" 1 to 9)

---

2 | Draw a line plot of the data shown. Use the line plot to identify the data's range, median, and mode.

Number of Push-ups			
Pam	ЖЖ II	Pru	ЖЖ III
Pat	ЖЖ	Pal	ЖЖ ЖЖ ЖЖ
Peg	ЖЖ III	Pia	ЖЖ II
Park	ЖЖ ЖЖ II	Paco	ЖЖ ЖЖ III
Paul	ЖЖ III	Pax	ЖЖ ЖЖ
Page	ЖЖ ЖЖ I	Penn	ЖЖ ЖЖ III

---

3 | Use the data shown to make a stem-and-leaf plot. Then explain how to read the plot.

Students Riding Bus 12			
52	49	45	34
30	20	18	14
40	29	24	54

Number of Students Riding Bus 12	
1	4 8
2	0
3	
4	
5	

---

4 | Show this data in a circle graph and in a bar graph. Which graph do you think is better for this data? Why?

Students' Favorite Fast Food	
hamburgers	25%
veggie burgers	5%
tacos	15%
pizza	40%
hot dogs	15%

---

5 | Do the practice page "Mighty Muscles."

---

6 | Use the line plot to find the range, mode, median, and mean of this data.

Minutes Spent on Homework

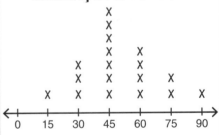

(line plot with X marks over 0, 15, 30, 45, 60, 75, 90)

---

7 | Ask 15 students in the same grade how long each one spent on homework last week. Next, draw a conclusion about your data. Then graph the data to clearly support your conclusion.

---

8 | Compare the 2011 and 2012 heating costs. Draw and then explain four conclusions you can make about the graph's data.

Cold Weather Heating Costs

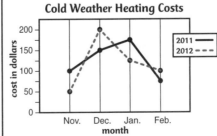

(line graph: y-axis "cost in dollars" 0 to 200, x-axis "month" Nov., Dec., Jan., Feb.; 2011 —, 2012 ---)

---

9 | Create a poster that shows how to create a double-bar graph.

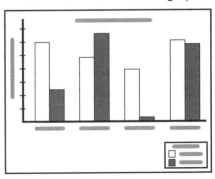

Choose & Do Math Grids • ©The Mailbox® Books • TEC61229 • Key p. 95

Note to the teacher: Program the student directions with the number of activities to be completed. Then copy the page and page 76 (back-to-back if desired) for each student.

Name _____   Date _____

Mighty Muscles

Use the tally table to make a line plot graph.
Then answer the questions.

Bench Press Contest Results	
pounds lifted	number of contestants
290	II
310	II
320	I
340	II
350	✝✝✝
360	IIII
370	✝✝✝ II
380	IIII
390	IIII
400	I

_____
title

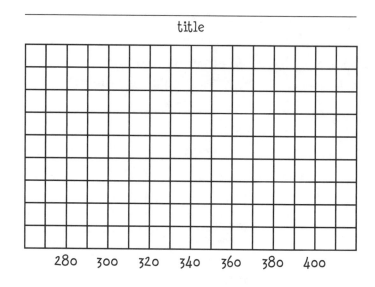

280   300   320   340   360   380   400

_____

1. How many pounds did the winning contestant lift? _____

2. How many contestants lifted 380 or more pounds? _____

3. How many contestants lifted 320 or fewer pounds? _____

4. How many contestants lifted more than 320 but less than 380 pounds? _____

5. What is the range of pounds lifted in the bench press contest? _____

6. How many pounds were lifted the most often? _____

7. What was the median number of pounds lifted? _____

8. What is the total number of contestants? _____

9. What is the mean, or average, number of pounds lifted by the contestants? _____

10. Which statistic do you think best reflects the contest results: the mean, median, or mode?

_____ Explain. _____

_____

Graphs

Name _____

Date _____

Choose ___ or more activities to do.
When you finish an activity, color its number.

---

1 Use the data to make a stem-and-leaf plot. Then draw a conclusion about hockey practice.

Hours of Hockey Practice

Week	Hours	Week	Hours
1	12	8	30
2	29	9	25
3	11	10	22
4	11	11	15
5	15	12	11
6	21	13	12
7	17	14	24

---

2 Make a line plot of the summer temperatures. Then identify the range, median, and mode or modes.

Temperatures

7	6 8
8	0 1 5 8 9 9
9	1 3 3 5

---

3 Draw a Venn diagram and label it as shown. Then fill it out to compare bar graphs and line graphs.

bar graph   line graph

---

4 Draw a diagram like the one shown. Then survey ten or more students and write each student's name in the space that tells whether he or she likes none, one, two, or three of these exercises. Finally, draw a conclusion about your diagram.

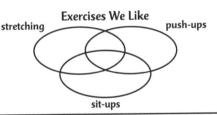

Exercises We Like
stretching   push-ups
sit-ups

---

5 Do the practice page "Fan Favorites."

#1

---

6 Use the test scores shown to create a line plot and a stem-and-leaf plot. Which graph do you think better displays the data? Explain.

90, 95, 96, 91, 90, 98, 99, 95, 95, 92, 93, 95, 99, 90, 97, 91, 90, 99

---

7 Use the data to make a double-line graph. Then write and answer four questions about the data.

Track Team Results

	Events Won	
Month	Gila Monsters	Sidewinders
February	63	42
March	75	58
April	71	63
May	70	71

---

8 Make a circle graph that shows how these students voted on their favorite team mascots. Then write three or more steps that explain how you made your graph.

Mascot	Number of Students
tiger	8
eagle	2
shark	6
chicken	1
wolf	3

---

9 Choose one of the types of graphs shown. Then create a poster to convince fellow students that it's the best type of graph.

Line Graph
Double-Line Graph
Stem-and-Leaf Plot
LINE PLOT
Circle Graph
Bar Graph
Double-Bar Graph

Choose & Do Math Grids • ©The Mailbox® Books • TEC61229 • Key p. 95

Note to the teacher: Program the student directions with the number of activities to be completed. Then copy the page and page 78 (back-to-back if desired) for each student.

77

Name _____

Date _____

Graphs

Fan Favorites

Use the data to complete the double-bar graph.
Then answer each question.

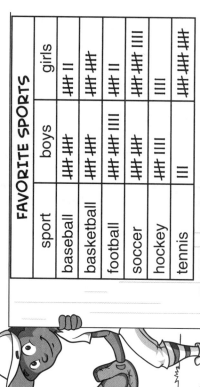

FAVORITE SPORTS

sport	boys	girls
baseball	ⅢⅢ ⅢⅢ	ⅢⅢ II
basketball	ⅢⅢ ⅢⅢ	ⅢⅢ ⅢⅢ
football	ⅢⅢ ⅢⅢ IIII	ⅢⅢ II
soccer	ⅢⅢ ⅢⅢ	ⅢⅢ ⅢⅢ IIII
hockey	ⅢⅢ IIII	IIII
tennis	III	ⅢⅢ ⅢⅢ ⅢⅢ

FAVORITE SPORTS

Number of Students: 16, 14, 12, 10, 8, 6, 4, 2, 0

baseball   basketball   football   soccer   hockey   tennis

Key ▨ = boys   ☐ = girls

1. Which sport do five times as many girls as boys prefer? _____

2. Which sport do twice as many boys as girls prefer? _____

3. Which two sports do girls like equally? _____

4. How many more girls than boys prefer tennis? _____

5. List the three sports that are the girls' favorites in order from most preferred to least. _____

6. List the four sports that are the boys' favorites from most preferred to least. _____

7. How many boys voted? _____   How many girls voted? _____

8. If 40 more children's votes were added to the graph, would you change the scale interval? _____   Why or why not? _____

9. Would a circle graph be a good way to display the data from the tally table? _____   Why or why not? _____

10. If you combined the boys' and girls' votes from the tally table, what kind of graph would you use to display the data? _____ Why? _____

Choose & Do Math Grids • ©The Mailbox® Books • TEC61229 • Key p. 96

Note to the teacher: Use with page 77.

Mean, Median, Mode, and Range

Name _____

Date _____

Choose ___ or more activities to do.
When you finish an activity, color its number.

---

1 Write yours and a friend's ten-digit phone numbers. Circle pairs of digits to make ten double-digit numbers. Find the mean, median, mode, and range of the double-digit numbers.

87, 75, 55, 01, 63

2 Survey five boys and five girls to find out how many minutes they spend watching television on a school night. Record your results and then find the mean, median, mode, and range for each group. Show your answers in a chart like the one shown.

Minutes Spent Watching Television

	mean	median	mode	range
boys				
girls				

3 Spin the spinner eight times. Record each number, put the numbers in order, and then circle the median number. Repeat four times. Then draw a conclusion about your results.

4 Find three different combinations of five numbers that have means of 27.

The mean of 25, 26, 28, 30, and 26 is 27.

5 Do the practice page "Mixed-Up Mail."

6 Find the median and the mean of each set of test scores. For each set, tell whether the median or the mean would be a better final grade.

A. 98, 89, 100, 86, 90, 93, 88

B. 80, 93, 89, 100, 84, 90, 80

7 Write five or more steps that explain how to find the range, median, and mode of the data on the stem-and-leaf plot shown.

Heights of Basketball Players
(in inches)

6	8 9
7	0 1 6 7 7
8	2 3 4

8 Separate a deck of playing cards into two piles: picture cards and number cards. Stack the cards facedown. Next, draw five number cards and one picture card. Then find the range, mean, median, or mode as guided by the code. Repeat five times.

Code
ace = range
king = mean
queen = median
jack = mode

9 Find the median for each set of data. Then draw a diagram that shows how to find the median when there is an even number of values.

A. 15, 24, 85, 44
B. 50, 21, 73, 24
C. 62, 64, 63, 62

Choose & Do Math Grids • ©The Mailbox® Books • TEC61229 • Key p. 96

Note to the teacher: Each student needs a paper clip to complete activity 3. Program the student directions with the number of activities to be completed. Then copy the page and page 80 (back-to-back if desired) for each student.

79

Mean, Median, Mode, and Range

Name _____   Date _____

Mixed-Up Mail

Part 1 Answer the questions using the digits in the zip code on each envelope.

1. Which envelope's zip code has a mean of seven? ____

2. For which envelope is the zip code's range five? ____

3. What is the range of the zip code on envelope C? ____

4. What is the mode for the zip code on envelope B? ____

5. What is the mean of the zip code on envelope E? ____

6. Which two envelopes' zip codes have the same median?
____   ____

7. Which two envelopes' zip codes have the same range?
____   ____

8. Which envelope's zip code has a range of four? ____

9. Which envelopes' zip codes do not have modes?
____   ____

10. For which envelope are the zip code's mean, median, and mode all 7? ____

Part 2 Color each envelope as guided.

11. If the zip code's mean is greater than three but less than five, color the envelope blue.

12. If the zip code's mean is greater than seven, color the envelope red.

13. If the zip code's mode is even, color the envelope green.

14. If the zip code's median is even, color the envelope yellow.

15. If the zip code's range is less than four, color the envelope orange.

Choose & Do Math Grids • ©The Mailbox® Books • TEC61229 • Key p. 96

Probability

Name _____

Date _____

Choose ___ or more activities to do.
When you finish an activity, color its number.

---

1 If you were to randomly draw one of the tickets shown, describe the probability of drawing the following:

A. an even number
B. a number less than 5
C. a number greater than 12
D. a number divisible by 3

⟩1⟨ ⟩2⟨ ⟩3⟨ ⟩4⟨
⟩5⟨ ⟩6⟨ ⟩7⟨ ⟩8⟨
⟩9⟨ ⟩10⟨ ⟩11⟨ ⟩12⟨

2 Draw a spinner with eight sections. Color the spinner so that it is impossible to spin orange, equally likely to spin yellow or blue, and unlikely to spin green. Then spin ten times and record each spin. Which color did you spin most often? Which color did you spin least often?

3 If you roll a die 15 times, how many times do you think you will roll each number? Copy the chart and record your predictions. Then roll a die 15 times and record a tally for each number rolled. Write a statement about your predictions and your results.

Die Number	Prediction	Tallies
1		
2		
3		
4		
5		
6		

4 Fold a piece of paper in half four times. In each section, write a number that is between four and 12. Then cut the paper along the fold lines to make 16 cards and put the cards in a bag. Draw a card, record the number, and return the card to the bag. Repeat ten times and then describe your results. Would your results be different if you did not return each card to the bag? Explain.

5 Do the practice page "Luck of the Claw."

6 Which events are the most and least likely? Explain.

A. Drawing a vowel from a full set of alphabet cards.

B. Drawing a prime number from a set of cards numbered 1–20.

C. Randomly choosing a month of the year that has 31 days.

7 If the letters in *mathematics* were printed on individual tiles and you drew one tile, which of the following is more likely? Explain.

MATHEMATICS

- drawing a consonant or drawing a vowel

- drawing the letter M or drawing the letter C

- drawing the letter M, T, or A or drawing the letter E, I, C, or S

8 There are three pairs of socks in a drawer. The socks are green, blue, and red. The socks are loose in the drawer. Draw tree diagrams that show all the possible outcomes if you were to grab two socks without looking. Then describe the likelihood of grabbing a pair of same-colored socks.

9 Imagine that you folded this shape into a cube and then rolled it like a die. Write a fraction to show the possibility of each statement below. Then write three statements that describe the probabilities of different outcomes.

	9		
8	7	8	9
	9		

A. rolling a number less than 7

B. rolling an even number

C. rolling an odd number

Note to the teacher: Each student needs a paper clip to complete activity 2 and a die to complete activity 3. Program the student directions with the number of activities to be completed. Then copy the page and page 82 (back-to-back if desired) for each student.

Probability

Name _____   Date _____

Luck of the Claw

- Complete each statement.

1. When Claudette drops the claw, it is certain that the claw will get a __ball_____ .

2. When Claudette drops the claw, the likelihood that the claw will get a _____ is impossible.

3. When Claudette drops the claw, it is equally likely the claw will get a _____
as a _____ .

4. When Claudette drops the claw, it is more likely the claw will get a _____ than
a _____ .

5. When Claudette drops the claw, it is unlikely the claw will get a _____ .

6. When Claudette drops the claw, it is less likely the claw will get a _____ than
a _____ .

7. When Claudette drops the claw, it is likely the claw will get a _____ .

8. When Claudette drops the claw, it is certain the claw will _____ .

$$P \text{ (probability)} = \frac{\text{number of balls described}}{\text{total number of balls}}$$

- Write a fraction to describe the probability of each outcome.

9. The claw will get a striped ball. $P = \frac{4}{20}$ or $\frac{1}{5}$

10. The claw will get a white ball. $P = $ _____

11. The claw will get a dotted ball. $P = $ _____

12. The claw will get a checked ball. $P = $ _____

13. The claw will get a white or striped ball. $P = $ _____

14. The claw will get a striped, dotted, or checked ball.
$P = $ _____

15. What do you think the likelihood is that Claudette will get a prize from the machine? Explain.

_____

_____

_____

_____

_____

Puzzlers

Name _____

Date _____

Choose ___ or more activities to do.
When you finish an activity, color its number.

1 A piggy bank has 12 coins. The total amount of the coins equals $1.23. What coins are in the bank? 	**2** Add the operations that will make each sentence true. A. (6 __ 6 __ 6) __ 6 __ 6 = 11 B. (7 __ 7) __ 7 __ 7 __ 7 = 7 C. (8 __ 8 __ 8) __ 8 __ 8 = 1 $5\ 5\ 5\ 5\ 5 = 11$ $(5 \times 5 + 5) \div 5 + 5 = 11$	**3** There are twice as many birds perched on a fence as there are cats laying in the grass. Altogether there are 24 legs. How many cats and birds are there?
4 Fill in the missing numbers so that the numbers across, down, and diagonally have a sum of 33. |		17
	11	
		9		**5** Do the practice page "Pampered Pets." 	**6** Today's date is Sunday, May 16. Deb's birthday is six days from the day after tomorrow. Bob's birthday is two days before Deb's birthday. On which days and dates are Deb's and Bob's birthdays?  **May 16**
7 What is the value of each figure? $\triangle + \triangle + \triangle = \bigcirc + \bigcirc$ $\square + \square + \square = \bigcirc + \bigcirc + \bigcirc + \bigcirc$ $\triangle + \triangle + \triangle + \triangle = \square + \square$ $\bigcirc + \bigcirc = \square + \triangle$ $\triangle =$ $\bigcirc =$ $\square =$	**8** Using four straight lines, divide the circle into sections so that only one star is in each section. 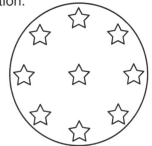	**9** Copy the model of a table and six chairs. Zach sits on the right in the middle. Zoe sits directly across from Mia. Jake sits on Mia's left. Ian sits on the end. Lucy sits on the right side in a diagonal line from Mia. Where does each student sit? Label your model.

Note to the teacher: Program the student directions with the number of activities to be completed. Then copy the page and page 84 (back-to-back if desired) for each student.

Name _____   Date _____

Pampered Pets

Use clues 1–5 to find out which pet belongs to each customer.
Put an X in each box that is not true and an O in each box that is true.

CLUES:

1. The kitten belongs to either Tom Katz or Gil Fish.

2. Gil Fish and Tom Katz each have a pet with four legs.

3. Chip Monk does not own a gerbil, and he is allergic to dogs.

4. Earl E. Bird's and Chip Monk's pets do not fly.

5. Tom Katz and Earl E. Bird are afraid of dogs.

	parrot	kitten	gerbil	dog	goldfish
Al E. Katt					
Chip Monk					
Earl E. Bird					
Tom Katz					
Gil Fish					

Use clues 6–10 to find each pet's name.

	parrot	kitten	gerbil	dog	goldfish
Dolly					
Golly					
Kelly					
Polly					
Gelly					

CLUES:

6. The first letter of each pet's name is not the same as the first letter of its animal name.

7. Kelly cannot fly or run.

8. Golly cannot fly or meow.

9. Dolly often imitates words people say.

10. Gelly cannot fly.

Complete each sentence.

11. Al E. Katt's pet is a _____ named _____.

12. Chip Monk's pet is a _____ named _____.

13. Earl E. Bird's pet is a _____ named _____.

14. Tom Katz's pet is a _____ named _____.

15. Gil Fish's pet is a _____ named _____.

Puzzlers

Name _____

Date _____

Choose ____ or more activities to do.
When you finish an activity, color its number.

---

1 Sarah has four pets: Sonny, Theo, Sam, and Frisky. Her hamster's name has six letters. Her cat's name begins with an *S*. Her fish is not named Sam, Frisky, or Theo. Sarah's fourth pet is a dog. Write the type and name of each pet.

2 Add parentheses ( ) and operation signs (+, −, x, ÷) to make each number sentence true.

$$9 \quad 8 \quad 7 \quad 6 \quad 5 \quad = \quad 20$$

$$9 \quad 8 \quad 7 \quad 6 \quad 5 \quad = \quad 78$$

5 4 3 2 1 = 20
5 x (4 − 3 + 2 + 1) = 20

3 A six-digit number contains two 6s, two 7s, and two 8s. The 6s are separated by one place, the 7s by two places, and the 8s by three places. What is the largest number you can make? What is the smallest number?

---

4 Find five consecutive numbers that total 800. Then find a pattern or relationship that helps you find five consecutive numbers that total 300.

5 Do the practice page "On the Road."

6 Draw a 5 x 5 grid like the one shown. Then arrange the numbers from the grid below on your grid so that the same number does not appear twice in any row or column.

0	10	30	0	40
20	20	40	20	10
40	10	30	40	0
30	0	10	30	10
40	20	0	30	20

---

7 Multiply 142,857 by the numbers 1 through 6. What pattern do you see?

142,857 x 1 = *n*

8 Today is Toby's birthday. He is five times as old as his brother Jamal. Jamal is six years younger than their sister Erica. Erica is twice the age of their sister Jade. If Jade is four, how old was Toby last week?

9 Assign a value to each letter of the alphabet so that A = $0.01 B = $0.02 C = $0.03, and so on, ending with Z = $0.26. Then find

A. two names that would have a value of $1.00 or more

B. two animals that would each have a value of $0.50 or less

C. a color with a value of $0.88

Choose & Do Math Grids • ©The Mailbox® Books • TEC61229 • Key p. 96

Note to the teacher: Program the student directions with the number of activities to be completed. Then copy the page and page 86 (back-to-back if desired) for each student.

85

Puzzlers

Name _____   Date _____

On the Road

Add multiplication or division symbols to make each sentence true.

1. 9 _×_ 4 _÷_ 3 _×_ 8 = 96

2. 4 ___ 12 ___ 6 ___ 9 = 32

3. 6 ___ 3 ___ 2 ___ 8 = 72

Work Space

4. 8 ___ 9 ___ 6 ___ 4 = 108

5. 20 ___ 5 ___ 1 ___ 6 = 24

6. 5 ___ 4 ___ 2 ___ 5 = 50

7. 4 ___ 25 ___ 5 ___ 10 = 2

8. 36 ___ 2 ___ 6 ___ 3 = 36

9. 24 ___ 6 ___ 12 ___ 16 = 3

10. 8 ___ 35 ___ 40 ___ 15 = 105

11. 48 ___ 6 ___ 8 ___ 4 = 16

12. 13 ___ 6 ___ 3 ___ 2 = 13

Are you sure this is the shortcut?

Puzzlers

Name _____

Date _____

Choose ___ or more activities to do.
When you finish an activity, color its number.

| **1** | How many paper clips are 6 pushpins and 2 staples worth? 8 pushpins and 5 staples? 2 pushpins and 48 staples? |

3 paper clips = 1 staple
2 staples = 1 pushpin

| **2** | Arrange the numbers on the grid so that the sum of each row and column is 45. |

3, 6, 9, 12, 15, 18, 21, 24, 27

| **3** | To make 48 a palindrome (a number that reads the same forward and backward), reverse the digits and add the two numbers. Then reverse the sum and add the two numbers. Make a palindrome for each number shown. |

$$\begin{array}{r} 48 \\ +\ 84 \\ \hline 132 \\ +231 \\ \hline 363 \end{array}$$

A. 2,651
B. 76
C. 785
D. 3,014
E. 684

| **4** | Copy the mystery problem shown three times. Then write 4, 5, 6, and 7 in the boxes as guided. |

(☐☐ × ☐) + ☐

A. Write the equation with the largest possible answer.
B. Write the equation with the smallest possible answer.
C. Write an equation that equals 384.

| **5** | Do the practice page "Stay the Course." |

| **6** | Using the clues, decide whether <, >, or = belongs in the circle. |

(2A + C) − B ◯ (2B + A) − C

A is two times as many as B.
C is five less than A.
B equals eight.

| **7** | Use the digits below, operation signs, and/or parentheses to make each statement true. |

A. 2 8 8 7 = 29
B. 2 8 8 7 = 150
C. 2 8 8 7 = 21

2 × 88 − 7 = 169

| **8** | Use the digits 0 through 9 in the boxes to complete each problem. Use each digit only once. |

☐☐☐ ÷ ☐ = 68

☐,☐☐☐ ÷ ☐☐ = 145

| **9** | Copy the scoreboard and use the clues to fill in the points earned each quarter. |

A. The Eagles won by ten points.
B. The Lions didn't score until the second quarter.
C. At the end of third quarter, the Eagles and the Lions were tied at 21 points.
D. The Eagles scored in every quarter.

	1st Quarter	2nd Quarter	3rd Quarter	4th Quarter	Total
Eagles	7				
Lions			7		24

Note to the teacher: Program the student directions with the number of activities to be completed. Then copy the page and page 88 (back-to-back if desired) for each student.

Name _____   Date _____

Stay the Course

Solve each problem. In each circle, write the number that completes the inequality. Then cross off the digits in the corresponding row. If you are correct, the sum of the remaining digits in each row will be 12.

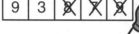

Shiver me timbers! I need help *burying* the treasure not *carrying* it!

A. 3 x 3 = _9_ > (8) > 14 ÷ 2 = _7_

9	3	X	X	X

B. 48 ÷ 8 = ___ < ◯ < 16 − (2 x 4) = ___

5	6	7	7	8

C. 36 − 29 = ___ > ◯ > 3 x 5 − 6 = ___

7	7	9	5	8

D. 4 x 5 ÷ 2 = ___ > ◯ > 96 ÷ 12 = ___

10	9	8	7	5

E. 72 ÷ 12 = ___ < ◯ < 72 ÷ 9 = ___

5	6	7	8	7

F. 18 − 3 x 4 = ___ > ◯ > 14 − 6 x 2 + 2 = ___

4	8	6	5	4

G. 42 ÷ 7 = ___ > ◯ > 56 ÷ 14 = ___

4	6	4	8	5

H. (12 ÷ 6) + (10 ÷ 2) = ___ > ◯ > 55 ÷ 11 = ___

7	7	6	5	5

I. 60 ÷ 12 = ___ < ◯ < 45 − 38 = ___

4	5	8	7	6

J. 84 ÷ 12 = ___ < ◯ < (3 x 6) − (6 + 3) = ___

7	7	5	8	9

K. (21 ÷ 3) + 1 = ___ < ◯ < 8 x 5 ÷ 4 = ___

8	2	10	9	10

L. 4 x 9 − 30 = ___ > ◯ > 3 + 2 x 5 − 9 = ___

7	6	5	5	4

M. 80 ÷ 10 = ___ > ◯ > 6 x 4 ÷ 4 = ___

8	6	7	6	6

N. 1 x 5 + 7 − 3 = ___ > ◯ > 91 ÷ 13 = ___

9	8	3	7	9

Page 5

Answers for 1, 3, 4, and 8 will vary.
2. 1,000,000; 800,000; 810,000; 808,000;
   807,600; 807,560
6. 9,999
7. A. 3,065; 3,165; 3,265
   B. 465,250; 475,250; 485,250
   C. 899,999; 999,999; 1,099,999
   D. 1,750,000; 1,650,000; 1,550,000
9. 4,742; 47,421; 436,084; 446,412;
   456,320; 474,000; 474,210; 474,216;
   474,316; 4,156,320

Page 6

I. A. orange
   B. green
   C. yellow
   D. red
   E. blue
   F. orange
   G. blue
   H. yellow
   I. purple
   J. green
II. I, F, H, E, A, D, G, B, C, J
III. A. 8,000,000 + 200,000 + 50,000 +
        9,000 + 800 + 10 + 8
     B. one million, three hundred twenty-five
        thousand, seven hundred fifty
     C. 1,000,000 + 300,000 + 20,000 +
        5,000 + 700 + 50

Page 7

Answers for 2 and 8 will vary.
1. Order will vary.
   3,425 + 9,738 = 13,163
   3,425 + 7,197 = 10,622
   3,425 + 5,645 = 9,070
   3,425 + 6,575 = 10,000
   3,425 + 8,896 = 12,321
3.

4. A. 986
   B. 7,328
   C. 491
   D. 29,813
   E. 71,535
   F. 8,271
6. A. rounded estimate: 10,000
      front-end estimate: 7,000
      sum: 9,369
   B. rounded estimate: 13,000
      front-end estimate: 12,700
      sum: 12,831
7.

	Add 999.		Add 5,879.
698	1,697	543	6,422
710	1,709	685	6,564
328	1,327	815	6,694
436	1,435	491	6,370

9. A. 20,341 + 68,547 = 88,888
   B. 23,954 + 56,054 = 80,008
   C. 77,936 + 20,841 = 98,777

Page 8

Across
A. 1,271
E. 101,985
H. 8,861
I. 5,167
K. 4,114
M. 457
O. 803
P. 95,337
Q. 58,206

Down
A. 108,545
B. 716
C. 1,014
D. 456
F. 95,105
G. 81,433
J. 76,279
L. 18,906
N. 7,182

A.1	2	B.7	C.1			D.4
0		E.1	0	1	F.9 G.8	5
H.8	8	6	1		I.5 1 6	J.7
5			K.4	L.1	1	4	6
M.4	5	N.7		O.8	0	3	2
5		1		P.9	5	3	3	7
		8		0			9
Q.5	8	2	0	6		

Page 9

Answers for 1–4, 6, 7, and 9 will vary.
8. A. 400, 464
   B. 600, 545
   C. 2,000; 1,109
   D. 2,000; 2,566
   E. 1,000; 733
464; 545; 733; 1,109; 2,566

Page 10

1. 2,000; 1,731
2. 2,000; 1,887
3. 600, 547
4. 6,000; 5,442
5. 9,000; 8,896
6. 4,000; 3,825
7. 500, 565
8. 1,000; 1,049
9. 5,000; 5,260
10. 7,000; 7,205

Answers for 11–14 will vary, but the differences
should be 5,191; 13,702; 456; and 182.

Page 11

Answers for 2–4 and 6–9 will vary.
1. 384 x 8 = 3,072
   697 x 9 = 6,273
   152 x 5 = 760
   361 x 6 = 2,166
   895 x 9 = 8,055
   472 x 7 = 3,304
   392 x 9 = 3,528
   194 x 9 = 1,746

Page 12

1. 5,904
2. 3,790
3. 1,468
4. 7,272
5. 408
6. 1,603
7. 1,158
8. 2,032
9. 5,202
10. 6,111
11. 2,034
12. 1,992
13. 3,715
14. 8,550
15. 1,734
16. 4,389

IT WAS BACK-TO-SCHOOL DAY!

Page 13

1. A. 25   **25**   B. 18   **18**
      x 39   **x 39**   x 42   **x 42**
      185   225   216   36
      + 75   +75   +432   + 72
      160   975   648   756

2. A. 1,813
   B. 1,173
   C. 1,593
   D. 1,363
3. A. 3[2]   B. 5[5]
       x 6[4]   x 2[1]
       2,048   1,155

   C. [4]8   D. 9[1]
       x 6[3]   x [3]1
       3,024   2,821

4. A. 52 x 24 = 1,248
   B. 36 x 12 = 432
   C. 31 x 60 = 1,860
   D. 16 x 26 = 416
6. A. 65 x 89 = 5,785
   B. 25 x 54 = 1,350
   C. 71 x 38 = 2,698
   D. 92 x 14 = 1,288
7. Field A
8. 12 x 48 and 24 x 24
9. Answers will vary.

Page 14

1. 975
2. 864
3. 2,666
4. 2,136
5. 2,016
6. 2,100
7. 3,266
8. 1,288
9. 1,155
10. 2,112
11. 1,850
12. 380
13. 4,095
14. 828
15. 847

IT KEEPS EVERYONE away!

Page 15

1. 521 x 48 = 25,008
   512 x 48 = 24,576
   152 x 48 = 7,296
   125 x 48 = 6,000
   251 x 48 = 12,048
   215 x 48 = 10,320
2. A. 124 x 13
   B. 333 x 25
   C. 206 x 32
   D. 407 x 18
3. Answers will vary.
4. A. 695 x 36 = 25,020
   B. 356 x 93 = 33,108
   C. 5,965 x 69 = 411,585
   D. 3,959 x 66 = 261,294
6. A. 6,509 x 38
   B. 5,389 x 60
7. 76
8.

A. 846 2	B. 145
30	2 18
16,920	4,610
C. 383 4	D. 783 6
23	38
8,832	28,188

9. A. =
   B. <
   C. >

Page 16

A. 24,416 B. 42,864 C. 69,483 D. 5,907 E. 5,149
H. 5,684 I. 56,322 L. 13,824 O. 83,968 R. 30,650
S. 11,424 T. 21,966
U. 7,248 V. 16,448

Because his players <u>DRIBBLE ALL OVER THE COURT</u>.

Page 17

Answers for 1, 6, and 8 will vary.

2. A. 154
   B. 138
   C. 145 R3
3. □ = 2
   △ = 8
   ○ = 1
   ☆ = 9
4. A. 218 ÷ 3 = 72 R2
   B. 715 ÷ 6 = 119 R1
7. 780 ÷ 2 = 390
   780 ÷ 4 = 195
   780 ÷ 6 = 130
   780 ÷ 8 = 97 R4
9. A. 69 R6
   B. 140 R2
   C. 125
   D. 73 R1

Page 18

A. 431 R1, 29 R4
B. 764, 20 R6
C. 238 R3, 50 R5
D. 732, 17 R4
E. 288, 43 R2
F. 436 R1, 29 R5

Page 19

1. C, D, and E
2. 46
3. A. 197 B. 98 R5 C. 49 R5

Each quotient is half of the previous quotient. So the quotient for C is one-fourth of the quotient for A.

4. 15
6. 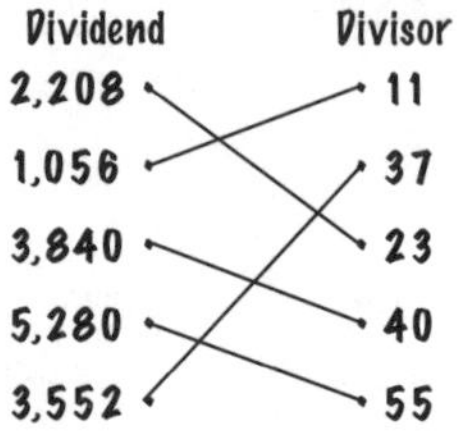
Dividend
Divisor
2,208
1,056
3,840
5,280
3,552
11
37
23
40
55
7. 220 minutes, or 3 hours 40 minutes
8. n = 4
9. A. 22 R14
   B. 13 R23
   C. 40 R2
   D. 25 R6
   E. 20 R14

13 R23, 20 R14, 22 R14, 25 R6, 40 R2

Page 20

Lane 1	$\begin{array}{r}171\\3\overline{)513}\end{array}$	$\begin{array}{r}11\text{ R}10\\39\overline{)439}\end{array}$	$\begin{array}{r}43\text{ R}3\\5\overline{)218}\end{array}$	$\begin{array}{r}6\text{ R}13\\51\overline{)319}\end{array}$	3rd
Lane 2	$\begin{array}{r}15\\42\overline{)630}\end{array}$	$\begin{array}{r}121\\6\overline{)726}\end{array}$	$\begin{array}{r}5\text{ R}9\\57\overline{)294}\end{array}$	$\begin{array}{r}86\text{ R}2\\5\overline{)432}\end{array}$	2nd
Lane 3	$\begin{array}{r}129\\4\overline{)516}\end{array}$	$\begin{array}{r}32\text{ R}12\\25\overline{)812}\end{array}$	$\begin{array}{r}98\\3\overline{)294}\end{array}$	$\begin{array}{r}12\\64\overline{)768}\end{array}$	1st

Lane 3 is the winner.

Page 21

1. 470 R1, 577, 653 R2, 710 R4, 755
2. Order will vary.
   2,415 ÷ 25 = 96 R15 5,367 ÷ 25 = 214 R17
   2,415 ÷ 43 = 56 R7 5,367 ÷ 43 = 124 R35
   2,415 ÷ 16 = 150 R15 5,367 ÷ 16 = 335 R7
   2,415 ÷ 57 = 42 R21 5,367 ÷ 57 = 94 R9
3. largest: 7,654 ÷ 23 = 332 R18
   smallest: 2,345 ÷ 76 = 30 R65
4. 2,565 ÷ 5 = 513; 5,439 ÷ 8 = 679 R7; 4,159 ÷ 3 = 1,386 R1; 8,472 ÷ 6 = 1,412
6. A. $\begin{array}{r}640\\13\overline{)8,\boxed{3}20}\end{array}$ C. $\begin{array}{r}308\text{ R}8\\29\overline{)\boxed{8},940}\end{array}$
   B. $\begin{array}{r}620\\16\overline{)9,9\boxed{2}0}\end{array}$ D. $\begin{array}{r}309\text{ R}13\\22\overline{)\boxed{6},811}\end{array}$

Page 21 (continued)

7.

	Divide by 39.
8,190	210
4875	125
9,360	240
9,750	250

8. A. 2,992 D. 232
   B. 434 E. 202
   C. 626 F. 191
   The first and last numeral of each quotient is the same.
9. Answers will vary.

Page 22

1. 834
2. 159
3. 672
4. 618
5. 753
6. 294
7. 165
8. 840
9. 327

[1] 8	3	4
[2] 1	5	9
[3] 6	7	2

Magic sum: 15

[4] 6	1	8
[5] 7	5	3
[6] 2	9	4

Magic sum: 15

[7] 1	6	5
[8] 8	4	0
[9] 3	2	7

Magic sum: 12

Page 23

Answers for 2, 3, 6, and 7 will vary.

1. A. B. C.

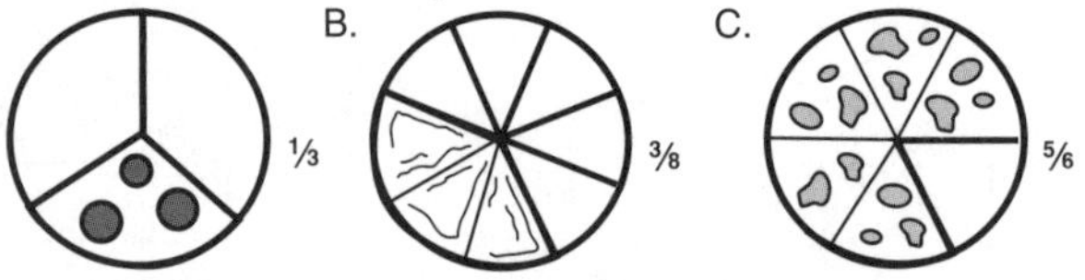
1/3
3/8
5/6

4. In the word *denominators*, 5/12 of the letters are vowels and 7/12 of the letters are consonants.
   In the word *fraction*, 3/8 of the letters are vowels and 5/8 of the letters are consonants.
   In the word *numerator*, 4/9 of the letters are vowels and 5/9 of the letters are consonants.
   In the word *part*, 1/4 of the letters are vowels and 3/4 of the letters are consonants.
   In the word *whole*, 2/5 of the letters are vowels and 3/5 of the letters are consonants.
8. 3/5 = 6/10
9. 1/5, 1/4, 1/3, 2/5, 1/2, 3/5, 2/3, 3/4, 5/6

Page 24

2/4 H, (5/6 F), [1/6 D]	1/2 G, [3/8 K], (5/8 L)	1/2 U, (3/4 E), [1/4 A]	(1/2 I), 1/3 O, [1/4 U]
[1/10 B], 3/5 D, (7/10 H)	[1/10 M], (1/2 P), 2/5 F	(11/12 N), 3/4 O, [7/12 A]	3/8 T, [1/4 S], (5/8 E)
[1/6 E], 1/3 O, (5/12 I)	[3/5 G], 7/10 L, (9/10 K)	(1/4 Y), [1/12 O], 1/6 A	(1/2 W), [1/5 Y], 3/10 E
(5/6 D), 2/3 K, [1/12 M]	4/5 A, [3/10 I], (9/10 U)		
7/8 M, [5/6 L], (11/12 G)	[1/8 F], 1/4 D, (3/4 H)		
[5/12 U], 2/3 E, (5/6 O)	[1/3 B], (7/8 C), 1/2 H		

He heard <u>HE'D MAKE A LOT OF DOUGH</u>!

Page 25

Answers for 1, 4, and 8 will vary.

2. A. GCF = 6
   B. GCF = 12
   C. GCF = 4
   D. GCF = 8
3. Possible answers include 23, 29, 31, 37, 41, 43, and 47.
6. 15/30 = 1/2, 12/32 = 3/8, 21/24 = 7/8, 9/12 = 3/4, 33/55 = 3/5, 12/15 = 4/5, 8/12 = 2/3, 25/100 = 1/4, 4/20 = 1/5, 25/30 = 5/6, 6/18 = 1/3, 4/32 = 1/8
7. 7/8, 5/6, 4/5, 2/3, 1/2, 1/4
9. 13/6, 39/18, 26/12, 52/22

Page 26

$\frac{7}{3} = 2\frac{1}{3}$ B | $\frac{15}{4} = 3\frac{3}{4}$ E | $\frac{25}{6} = 4\frac{1}{6}$ C | $\frac{16}{8} = 2$ A | $\frac{11}{2} = 5\frac{1}{2}$ U | $\frac{14}{4} = 3\frac{1}{2}$ S | $\frac{45}{12} = 3\frac{3}{4}$ E

$\frac{11}{5} = 2\frac{1}{5}$ T | $\frac{16}{3} = 5\frac{1}{3}$ H | $\frac{60}{16} = 3\frac{3}{4}$ E | $\frac{15}{8} = 1\frac{7}{8}$ Y

$\frac{19}{4} = 4\frac{3}{4}$ P | $\frac{22}{6} = 3\frac{2}{3}$ L | $\frac{18}{9} = 2$ A | $\frac{30}{16} = 1\frac{7}{8}$ Y | $\frac{22}{12} = 1\frac{5}{6}$ O | $\frac{47}{8} = 5\frac{7}{8}$ N

$\frac{21}{8} = 2\frac{5}{8}$ D | $\frac{17}{6} = 2\frac{5}{6}$ I | $\frac{10}{5} = 2$ A | $\frac{13}{3} = 4\frac{1}{3}$ M | $\frac{11}{6} = 1\frac{5}{6}$ O | $\frac{94}{16} = 5\frac{7}{8}$ N | $\frac{42}{16} = 2\frac{5}{8}$ D | $\frac{7}{2} = 3\frac{1}{2}$ S

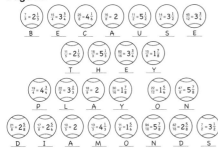

Page 27

Answers for 2, 3, 6, and 7 will vary.

1. A. $\frac{1}{2}$ B. $\frac{3}{4}$ C. $\frac{2}{3}$ D. $\frac{5}{6}$
4. A. $1\frac{1}{5}$ B. $1\frac{5}{8}$ C. $2\frac{3}{4}$
8. $5\frac{7}{8} - 1\frac{4}{8} = 4\frac{3}{8}$ $7\frac{5}{8} - 3\frac{4}{8} = 4\frac{1}{8}$
9. A. $\frac{2}{3}$ D. $\frac{7}{10}$

Page 28

O. $\frac{2}{3}$ I. $\frac{2}{5}$ A. $\frac{5}{12}$ U. $\frac{7}{12}$ P. $\frac{1}{5}$
W. 1 T. $\frac{9}{10}$ F. $\frac{1}{4}$ C. $1\frac{1}{8}$ R. $1\frac{1}{3}$
L. $\frac{1}{2}$ Y. $\frac{1}{3}$ E. $\frac{4}{5}$ V. $\frac{5}{6}$ S. $1\frac{2}{5}$

A "PAWS-ITIVELY" "PURR-FECT" SCORE!

Page 29

Answers for 2, 4, and 6 will vary.

1. A = $\frac{3}{5}$, B = $\frac{6}{10}$
3. A. 3 B. 1 C. 1 D. 3
7. $\frac{1}{3}$
8.

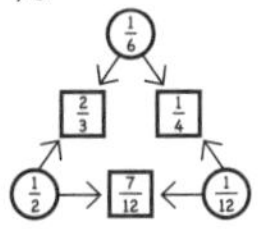

9. A. $\frac{17}{24}$ B. $\frac{13}{24}$ C. $\frac{11}{12}$

Page 30

1. $1\frac{1}{2}$ 2. $\frac{7}{8}$ 3. $\frac{16}{21}$
4. $1\frac{1}{8}$ 5. $\frac{1}{6}$ 6. $\frac{2}{5}$
7. $\frac{7}{40}$ 8. $\frac{3}{10}$ 9. $\frac{7}{8}$
10. $1\frac{1}{8}$ 11. $\frac{17}{18}$ 12. $\frac{1}{24}$
13. $\frac{1}{15}$ 14. $1\frac{5}{8}$ 15. $\frac{2}{15}$

Page 31

Answers for 1 and 9 will vary.

2. A. The first problem has the greater difference. $2\frac{5}{8} - 1\frac{1}{4} = 1\frac{3}{8}$; $2\frac{5}{9} - 1\frac{1}{5} = 1\frac{16}{45}$
   B. The first problem has the greater difference. $4\frac{2}{5} - 2\frac{3}{8} = 2\frac{1}{40}$; $4\frac{1}{5} - 2\frac{2}{8} = 1\frac{19}{20}$
   C. The first problem has the greater difference. $6\frac{1}{4} - 3\frac{1}{8} = 3\frac{1}{8}$; $6\frac{1}{5} - 3\frac{1}{7} = 3\frac{2}{35}$
3. $18\frac{1}{12}$ pounds
4. Order will vary.
   $8\frac{1}{2} + 2\frac{1}{4} = 10\frac{3}{4}$ $8\frac{1}{2} + 15\frac{5}{8} = 24\frac{1}{8}$
   $8\frac{1}{2} + 6\frac{2}{3} = 15\frac{1}{6}$ $8\frac{1}{2} + 3\frac{1}{6} = 11\frac{2}{3}$
   $8\frac{1}{2} + 3\frac{3}{5} = 12\frac{1}{10}$ $8\frac{1}{2} + 9\frac{7}{10} = 18\frac{1}{5}$
6.

	Add $1\frac{1}{3}$.	Subtract $1\frac{1}{3}$.
$6\frac{1}{5}$	$7\frac{8}{15}$	$4\frac{13}{15}$
$4\frac{1}{8}$	$5\frac{11}{24}$	$2\frac{19}{24}$
$7\frac{7}{12}$	$8\frac{11}{12}$	$6\frac{1}{4}$
$1\frac{5}{6}$	$3\frac{1}{6}$	$\frac{1}{2}$

7. $10\frac{9}{20}$
8. $3\frac{9}{40}$

Page 32

Dozens of Eggs Laid by Farmer Brown's Hens					
Hen	**May**	**June**	**July**	**August**	**Total**
Gladys	2	$2\frac{1}{2}$	$1\frac{1}{3}$	$1\frac{1}{4}$	$7\frac{1}{12}$
Maude	$2\frac{1}{2}$	$2\frac{1}{3}$	$1\frac{3}{4}$	$1\frac{2}{3}$	$8\frac{1}{4}$
Shelly	$1\frac{11}{12}$	$1\frac{3}{4}$	$2\frac{1}{12}$	$1\frac{7}{12}$	$7\frac{1}{3}$
Total	$6\frac{5}{12}$	$6\frac{7}{12}$	$5\frac{1}{6}$	$4\frac{1}{2}$	$22\frac{2}{3}$

Page 32 (continued)

1. June
2. Maude
3. Gladys, $\frac{1}{4}$ dozen eggs
4. Maude, $\frac{5}{12}$ dozen eggs
5. Gladys, $\frac{1}{12}$ dozen eggs
6. August
7. $\frac{11}{12}$ dozen eggs
8. $14\frac{5}{12}$ dozen eggs
9. June, $\frac{1}{6}$ dozen eggs
10. $16\frac{1}{4}$ dozen eggs

Page 33

1.

x	2	3	4
$\frac{1}{4}$	$\frac{1}{2}$	$\frac{3}{4}$	1
$\frac{1}{2}$	1	$1\frac{1}{2}$	2
$\frac{3}{4}$	$1\frac{1}{2}$	$2\frac{1}{4}$	3

2. The product for Step 4 is the original number. The steps cancel each other out.
3. $\frac{1}{3}$ of 63# = 21#
   A. 15# B. 21# C. 5# D. 21#
   Boxes B and D will balance the scales.
4. A. $\frac{4}{25}$ B. $\frac{4}{7}$ C. $8\frac{3}{4}$ D. $1\frac{3}{7}$
   $\frac{4}{25}$, $\frac{4}{7}$, $1\frac{3}{7}$, $8\frac{3}{4}$
6. Answers will vary.
7. A. 36 square units
   B. 10 square units
   C. 9 square units
8. $n = \frac{3}{16}$
9. A. 36 keys are black. 52 keys are white. $\frac{13}{22}$ of the keys are white.
   B. 10 keys are black. 14 keys are white. $\frac{7}{12}$ of the keys are white.

Page 34

A. $1\frac{1}{4}$ B. $\frac{1}{2}$ C. $\frac{5}{16}$ D. $6\frac{3}{5}$
E. $1\frac{2}{5}$ F. $\frac{1}{2}$ G. $2\frac{1}{4}$ H. $\frac{27}{40}$
I. $2\frac{1}{2}$ J. $\frac{2}{5}$ K. 4 L. $\frac{5}{8}$
M. $\frac{1}{30}$ N. $7\frac{7}{8}$ O. $\frac{8}{15}$ P. $2\frac{11}{12}$
Q. $\frac{7}{20}$ R. $4\frac{1}{2}$ S. $5\frac{1}{4}$ T. $\frac{25}{48}$

Page 35

Answers for 1, 6, and 7 will vary.

2. three quilts: $14\frac{5}{8}$ yards purple stripe, $9\frac{3}{4}$ yards blue dots, $10\frac{1}{4}$ yards solid green
   four quilts: $19\frac{1}{2}$ yards purple stripe, 13 yards blue dots, $13\frac{2}{3}$ yards solid green
   five quilts: $24\frac{3}{8}$ yards purple stripe, $16\frac{1}{4}$ yards blue dots, $17\frac{1}{12}$ yards solid green
   six quilts: $29\frac{1}{4}$ yards purple stripe, $19\frac{1}{2}$ yards blue dots, $20\frac{1}{2}$ yards solid green
3. A. $7 < 7\frac{1}{2}$
   B. $20\frac{4}{5} < 21$
   C. $14 < 14\frac{2}{3}$
4. RED = $1\frac{61}{72}$
   WHITE = $1\frac{13}{64}$
   BLUE = $1\frac{22}{27}$
8. $3\frac{3}{5} \times \frac{2}{3} = 2\frac{2}{5}$
   $4\frac{1}{2} \times \frac{2}{3} = 3$
   $2\frac{1}{6} \times \frac{2}{3} = 1\frac{4}{9}$
   $1\frac{3}{4} \times \frac{2}{3} = 1\frac{1}{6}$
   $5\frac{5}{8} \times \frac{2}{3} = 3\frac{3}{4}$
9. A. $3\frac{3}{5}$ B. $3\frac{13}{24}$ C. $2\frac{1}{24}$ D. $1\frac{1}{48}$

Page 36

E $19\frac{1}{2}$
E 21
O 14
S $\frac{17}{50}$
A $3\frac{1}{2}$
M $1\frac{4}{5}$
H $2\frac{11}{18}$
C $1\frac{9}{16}$
R $5\frac{7}{9}$
R $3\frac{5}{6}$
Y $1\frac{5}{12}$
T 19
W $17\frac{1}{2}$
R $15\frac{2}{3}$
T $8\frac{13}{24}$

"'HAY', WHERE'S MY TRACTOR?"

Page 37

1. A. $(1 \times 10) + (1 \times 1) + (9 \times 0.01) = 11\frac{9}{100}$
   B. $(2 \times 10) + (1 \times 1) + (6 \times 0.1) = 21\frac{6}{10}$, or $21\frac{3}{5}$
   C. $6 \times 0.01 = \frac{6}{100}$, or $\frac{3}{50}$
   D. $5 \times 0.1 = \frac{5}{10}$, or $\frac{1}{2}$
   E. $(6 \times 1) + (1 \times 0.1) + (5 \times 0.01) = 6\frac{15}{100}$, or $6\frac{3}{20}$
   F. $(7 \times 1) + (4 \times 0.1) + (1 \times 0.01) = 7\frac{41}{100}$
2. A. 2.3, 2.4; 2.6, 2.7
   B. 3.3, 3.4; 3.6, 3.7
   C. 4.81, 4.82; 4.84, 4.85
   D. 5.04, 5.05; 5.07, 5.08
   E. 11.6, 11.7; 11.9, 12.0
   F. 2.37, 2.38; 2.40, 2.41
   G. 9.0, 9.1; 9.3, 9.4
   H. 16.2, 16.3; 16.5, 16.6
3.

Fraction	Decimal
$\frac{4}{5}$	0.8
$\frac{3}{25}$	0.12
$\frac{1}{4}$	0.25
$8\frac{1}{10}$	8.1
$\frac{3}{20}$	0.15
$\frac{7}{20}$	.035
$1\frac{47}{100}$	1.47
$\frac{2}{25}$	0.08
$11\frac{9}{10}$	11.9
$9\frac{2}{5}$	9.4

4. $\frac{1}{4} = 0.25$ $\frac{1}{2} = 0.5$ $\frac{3}{4} = 0.75$
   $\frac{1}{3} = 0.333\ldots$ $\frac{2}{3} = 0.666\ldots$ $\frac{1}{5} = 0.2$
   $\frac{2}{5} = 0.4$ $\frac{3}{5} = 0.6$ $\frac{4}{5} = 0.8$
   $\frac{5}{10} = 0.5$
6. 2.14 = two and fourteen hundredths
   207.05 = two hundred seven and five hundredths
   8,000.8 = eight thousand and eight tenths
   145.9 = one hundred forty-five and nine tenths
   63.52 = sixty-three and fifty-two hundredths
7. 12.99, 12.95, 12.94, 12.9, 12.8, 12.75, 12.6, 12.59, 12.52, 12.5, 12.47, 12.3, 12.18, 12.17, 12.1, 12.08, 12.07, 12.05, 12.04, 12.02
8. Answers will vary.
9.

Number	Rounded to the Nearest Whole Number	Rounded to the Nearest Tenth
0.89	1	0.9
1.28	1	1.3
5.14	5	5.1
6.39	6	6.4
4.52	5	4.5
7.45	7	7.5
9.61	10	9.6

Page 38

A	103.4	tens	ones	tenths
B	47.31	tenths	tens	ones
C	934.2	tens	ones	hundredths
D	7,561.04	hundredths	tenths	hundreds
E	340.5	hundreds	tens	ones
F	64.26	tens	tenths	ones
G	2.47	ones	hundredths	tenths
H	2,783.94	hundreds	tenths	hundredths
I	40.11	ones	tens	tenths
J	745.77	tens	hundreds	ones
K	58.4	tenths	hundredths	tens
L	747.3	ones	tens	hundreds
M	2,496.08	thousands	ones	hundreds
N	19.48	ones	tenths	hundredths
O	3,164.2	tens	ones	thousands
P	405.81	thousands	tens	hundreds
Q	8.49	tens	ones	tenths
R	6,149.25	tenths	tens	hundredths
S	360.42	tenths	ones	tens
T	9.84	hundredths	tenths	tens

Page 39

1. A. one hundred, one thousandth
   B. ten, one hundredth
   C. one, one tenth
   D. ten thousand, one hundredth
   E. one hundred, one tenth
   F. one hundred, one thousandth
2. 0.689 0.134 0.245 0.325 0.103 0.658
3. A. twelve and three hundred eight thousandths, 10 + 2 + 0.3 + 0.008
   B. nine and seventy-four thousandths, 9 + 0.07 + 0.004
   C. sixty and one hundred fifty-two thousandths, 60 + 0.1 + 0.05 + 0.002
   D. two hundred and four hundred eighteen thousandths, 200 + 0.4 + 0.01 + 0.008
   E. fifty-three and sixteen thousandths, 50 + 3 + 0.01 + 0.006
4. A. ○○ and △△△◇
   B. ○ and □□◇◇
   C. ○○○ and △□◇◇
   D. ◇
   E. ○ and △◇◇◇
   F. ○○ and □□□◇◇◇
6. A. 13.12(2), two thousandths
   B. 10.9(7)4, seven hundredths
   C. 1.7(5)4, five hundredths
   D. 15.2(9)4, nine hundredths
   E. 4.5(1)4, one hundredth
   F. 0.14(8), eight thousandths
   G. 5.16(1), one thousandth
   H. 6.18(7), seven thousandths
7.

has three tenths	has six hundredths	has two thousandths
0.326 2.306 62.306	0.063 3.26 20.063	0.632 6.032 36.002

8. 76.110, 76.552, 87.431, 95.431, 96.320, 97.320
9.

Number	+ one tenth	+ one hundredth	+ one thousandth
1.823	1.923	1.833	1.824
6.752	6.852	6.762	6.753
9.360	9.460	9.370	9.361
5.148	5.248	5.158	5.149
3.071	3.171	3.081	3.072
8.205	8.305	8.215	8.206

Page 40

A. 5.003
B. 125.1
C. 300.021
D. 1.012
E. 78.02
F. 14.55
G. 17.9
H. 64.07
I. 31.09
J. 45.116
K. six and three hundred twenty-five thousandths
L. two hundred four and eight hundredths
M. one hundred eighty-two and four hundred seven thousandths
N. sixteen thousandths

Page 41

Answers for 1, 2, and 4 will vary.
3. Students' diagrams will vary.
   A. 1.6 B. 0.816 C. 0.88
6. A. 13.962
   B. 6.324
   C. 7.286, 73.878
   D. 26.823, 15.370
7. 25.059 + 22.101 = 47.16,
   25.059 + 9.08 = 34.139,
   25.059 + 11.423 = 36.482,
   25.059 + 0.758 = 25.817;
   25.059 – 22.101 = 2.958,
   25.059 – 9.08 = 15.979,
   25.059 – 11.423 = 13.636,
   25.059 – 0.758 = 24.301
8. A. 6.663 B. 0.964 C. 7.888
   D. 54.243 E. 95.778
9. The end number is the same as the starting number because the calculations in between equal 0.

Page 42

1. 9.765
2. 126.50
3. 28.46
4. 0.818
5. 13.828
6. 5.991
7. 16.567
8. 2.394
9. 27.522
10. 40.994
11. 37.458
12. 10.329
13. 34.48
14. 12.295
15. 2.079
16. 10.809

DO YOU WANT TO HEAR MY PROBLEMS?

Page 43

Answers for 1, 4, and 8 will vary.
2. A. 0.359 x 30 = 10.77
   B. 0.395 x 0.3 = 0.1185
   C. 3.576 x 30 = 107.28
   D. 0.336 x 3 = 1.008
3. A. 1.3 x 3.4 = 4.42
   B. 42.1 x 21.3 = 896.73
   C. 23.4 x 12.3 = 287.82
   D. 124.3 x 3.2 = 397.76
6. A. 0.3 > 0.003
   B. 1.224 = 1.224
   C. 1.53 = 1.53
   D. 0.819 > 0.621
7. Code
   ☆ = 0 A. 0.36
   # = 2 B. 6.05
   ◎ = 3 C. 30.5
   ☽ = 5 D. 0.062
   ✿ = 6 E. 36.25
9. The placeholder was not used when multiplying the 3, so that product is not correct. Also the decimal point was carried down as in an addition problem, so the place value of the final product is incorrect.
   1.4
   x 3.9
   126
   + 420
   5.46

Page 44

A. 5.55
B. 160.0
C. 5.84
D. 0.42
E. 7.14
F. 13.806
G. 0.990
H. 28.404
I. 498.33
J. 3.192
K. 374.883
L. 180.81

Give it a hand!

Page 45

Answers for 3 and 4 will vary.
1. A. 32.4 D. 8.5
   B. 0.91 E. 26.05
   C. 20.7 F. 13.52
32.4, 26.05, 20.7, 13.52, 8.5, 0.91
2. A. 9)83.7 = 9.3 C. 3)26.73 = 8.91
   B. 5)49.05 = 9.81 D. 6)50.22 = 8.37
6. A. greatest: [2])8.64 = [4].[3][2] least: [9])8.64 = [0].[9][6]
   B. greatest: [3])5.67 = [1].[8][9] least: [9])5.67 = [0].[6][3]
7. A. 5.44 ÷ 4 = 1.36 E. 149.6 ÷ 2 = 74.8
   D. 78.6 ÷ 6 = 13.1 F. 14.84 ÷ 7 = 2.12
8. soda = $0.43 per unit
   cupcakes = $0.78 per unit
   juice boxes = $0.96 per unit
   candy bar = $0.98 per unit
   Explanations will vary.
9. 648.72 ÷ 9 = 72.08 388.35 ÷ 9 = 43.15
   392.4 ÷ 9 = 43.6 743.4 ÷ 9 = 82.6
   35.01 ÷ 9 = 3.89 50.4 ÷ 9 = 5.6

Page 46

1. 13.7, D
2. 0.839, R
3. 0.348, S
4. 34.4, S
5. 0.079, E
6. 17.9, S
7. 0.014, A
8. 62.9, R
9. 0.849, T
10. 50.9, E
11. 16.57, E
12. 0.043, D
13. 82.3, T
14. 0.236, E

A DESERT DESSERT!

Page 47

Answers for 1, 3, 4, 8, and 9 will vary.
2. A. = B. ≠ C. = D. ≠ E. ≠
6. A. = B. = C. ≠
7. A. $\frac{1}{4}$ B. $\frac{1}{3}$ C. $\frac{2}{5}$ D. $\frac{1}{3}$ E. $\frac{1}{3}$

Page 48

A. yellow
B. red
C. yellow
D. red
E. yellow
F. red
G. yellow
H. red
I. yellow
J. yellow
K. red
L. yellow
M. red
N. yellow
O. red
P. yellow
Q. yellow
R. red
S. yellow

Answers will vary.
B. 1:4 = $\frac{2}{8}$ or 1:5 = $\frac{2}{10}$
D. 7:12 = $\frac{14}{24}$ or 5:8 = $\frac{15}{24}$
F. $\frac{1}{2}$ = 6:12 or $\frac{12}{26}$ = 6:13
H. 5:6 = $\frac{25}{30}$ or 4:5 = $\frac{24}{30}$
K. $\frac{3}{10}$ = 6:20 or $\frac{12}{42}$ = 6:21
M. $\frac{8}{21}$ = 8:21 or $\frac{4}{6}$ = 8:12
O. 3:25 = $\frac{6}{50}$ or 3:50 = $\frac{6}{100}$
R. $\frac{7}{50}$ = 7:50 or $\frac{7}{100}$ = 7:100

Page 49

Answers for 6 and 9 will vary.
1. A. $\frac{3}{10}$, 0.3, 30%
   B. $\frac{5}{10}$, 0.5, 50%
   C. $\frac{2}{10}$, 0.2, 20%
2. A. $\frac{25}{100}$, 0.25, 25%
   B. $\frac{15}{100}$, 0.15, 15%
   C. $\frac{20}{100}$, 0.20, 20%
   D. $\frac{40}{100}$, 0.40, 40%
3.

fraction	equivalent fraction	decimal	percent
$\frac{1}{4}$	$\frac{25}{100}$	0.25	25%
$\frac{2}{25}$	$\frac{8}{100}$	0.08	8%
$\frac{3}{20}$	$\frac{15}{100}$	0.15	15%
$\frac{3}{5}$	$\frac{60}{100}$	0.60	60%
$\frac{1}{2}$	$\frac{50}{100}$	0.50	50%
$\frac{2}{50}$	$\frac{4}{100}$	0.04	4%

4. red = $\frac{12}{100}$, 0.12, 12%
   yellow = $\frac{16}{100}$, 0.16, 16%
   orange = $\frac{20}{100}$, 0.20, 20%
   green = $\frac{24}{100}$, 0.24, 24%
   blue = $\frac{28}{100}$, 0.28, 28%
7.

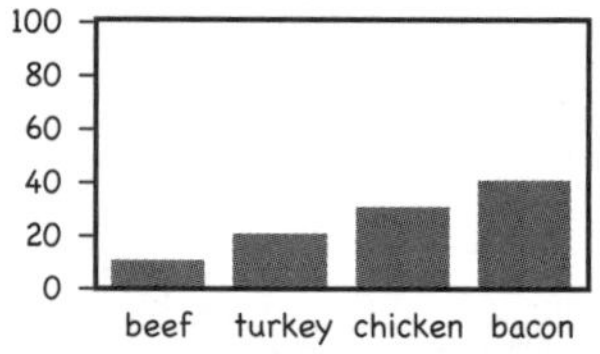

8. A. shaded portion: $\frac{6}{10}$, 0.6, 60%; unshaded portion: $\frac{4}{10}$, 0.4, 40%
   B. shaded portion: $\frac{2}{5}$, 0.4, 40%; unshaded portion: $\frac{3}{5}$, 0.6, 60%

Page 50

A. $\frac{20}{100} = \frac{1}{5}$
B. $\frac{62}{100} = \frac{31}{50}$
C. $\frac{8}{100} = \frac{2}{25}$
D. $\frac{35}{100} = \frac{7}{20}$
E. $\frac{58}{100} = \frac{29}{50}$
F. $\frac{90}{100} = \frac{9}{10}$
G. $\frac{26}{100} = \frac{13}{50}$
H. $\frac{12}{100} = \frac{3}{25}$
I. $\frac{40}{100} = \frac{2}{5}$
J. $\frac{88}{100} = \frac{22}{25}$
K. $\frac{65}{100} = \frac{13}{20}$
L. $\frac{4}{100} = \frac{1}{25}$
M. $\frac{10}{100} = \frac{1}{10}$
N. $\frac{22}{100} = \frac{11}{50}$
O. $\frac{54}{100} = \frac{27}{50}$
P. $\frac{75}{100} = \frac{3}{4}$

Page 51

Answers for 1–4, 6, and 9 will vary.
7.

length	width	perimeter
36 ft.	**54 ft.**	180 ft.
41 in.	25 in.	132 in.
65 cm	**65 cm**	260 cm
72 m	72 m	288 m
112 ft.	**68 ft.**	360 ft.

8. A. 8 B. 5

Page 52

A. 15
B. 15
C. 16.5
D. 17.5
E. 15.5
F. 12.5
G. 11.5
H. 14.5
I. 13.5
J. 13
K. 14.5
L. 14
M. 12.5
N. 11
O. 16
P. 13.5
Q. 12
R. 11.5
S. 15.5
T. 12.5

Page 53

1. Rectangle dimensions are 2 x 16, 3 x 15, 4 x 14, 5 x 13, 6 x 12, 7 x 11, 8 x 10, and 9 x 9.
2. $p = 34$ m, $a = 62$ m^2; Explanations will vary.
3. A. 480 sq. ft.
   B. 532 sq. ft.
   C. 420 sq. ft.
   D. 468 sq. ft.
   The combined areas of figures B and D is 1,000 sq. ft.
4. 10" x 18", $p = 56$", $a = 180$ in.^{2}; Explanations will vary.
6. Rectangle B; explanations will vary.
7. Would Be a Square: 25, 49, 121
   Could Be a Square: 36, 81, 100, 144
   Could Not Be a Square: 27, 42, 54
8. Answers will vary.
9.

Rectangle Measurements

Length	Width	Perimeter	Area
9	7	32	63
7	6	26	42
5	5	20	25
6	8	28	48
10	5	30	50
3	9	24	27

Page 54

A. $p = 130$ ft.
   $a = 1{,}050$ ft.^{2}
B. $p = 116$ ft.
   $a = 648$ ft.^{2}
C. $p = 84$ ft.
   $a = 288$ ft.^{2}
D. $p = 52$ m
   $a = 69$ m^2
E. $p = 42$ m
   $a = 86$ m^2
F. $p = 70$ ft.
   $a = 250$ ft.^{2}
G. $p = 30$ yd.
   $a = 26$ yd.^{2}
H. $p = 28$ ft.
   $a = 32$ ft.^{2}

Page 55

Answers for 8 and 9 will vary.
1.

cups	pints	quarts	gallons
16	8	4	1
96	48	24	6
32	16	8	2
128	64	32	8

2. A. <
   B. =
   C. =
   D. <
   E. =
3. To convert 15 feet to yards, divide 15 by 3; 15 feet = 5 yards
   To convert 6 gallons to quarts, multiply 6 by 4; 6 gallons = 24 quarts
   To convert 3 yards to inches, multiply 3 by 36; 3 yards = 108 inches
4. 120 pounds, 320 ounces, 15 pounds, 160 ounces, 56 ounces, 3 pounds, 40 ounces, 2 pounds
6. B. 4
   C. 16
   D. ounces
   E. weight
7. A. 14
   B. 134
   C. 3
   D. 7.5
   E. 3⅓

Page 56

1. football helmet	1 oz.	**1 lb.**	1 T
2. T-shirt	**10 oz.**	10 lb.	10 T
3. pillow	**22 oz.**	22 lb.	22 T
4. toy car	**6 oz.**	6 lb.	6 T
5. shoebox	**8 oz.**	8 lb.	8 T
6. television	43 oz.	**43 lb.**	43 T
7. adult male	$\frac{1}{10}$ oz.	$\frac{1}{10}$ lb.	**$\frac{1}{10}$ T**
8. basket of toys	4 oz.	**4 lb.**	4 T
9. tractor trailer	16 oz.	16 lb.	**16 T**
10. box of books	15 oz.	**15 lb.**	15 T
11. foam ball	**3 oz.**	3 lb.	3 T
12. action figure	**5 oz.**	5 lb.	5 T
13. box of crayons	**2 oz.**	2 lb.	2 T
14. bowling ball	8 oz.	**8 lb.**	8 T
15. horse	$\frac{3}{4}$ oz.	$\frac{3}{4}$ lb.	**$\frac{3}{4}$ T**
16. electric guitar	7 oz.	**7 lb.**	7 T
17. pair of sunglasses	**3 oz.**	3 lb.	3 T
18. baseball bat	**32 oz.**	32 lb.	32 T

Page 57

1. 5 millimeters; 4 centimeters; 65 millimeters; 7.5 centimeters; 92.5 millimeters; 90 centimeters; 95 centimeters; 1 meter; 1,010 millimeters; 1.1 meters
2. A liter is a unit of capacity measurement. The rest are units of length measurement.
3.

mm	cm	m
1,000	100	1
2,500	250	2.5
500	50	0.5
12,000	1,200	12

4.

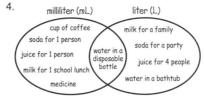

6. A. 25,000 mg
   B. 4,000 g
   C. 3.7 kg
   D. 215,000 mg
   E. 500,000 mg
7. Answers will vary.
8. AB = 1.5 cm = 15 mm, AC = 1.1 cm = 11 mm, AF = 1.9 cm = 19 mm, BC = 1 cm = 10 mm, BE = 1.6 cm = 16 mm, BF = 1.2 cm = 12 mm, CF = 0.8 cm = 8 mm, CE = 0.6 cm = 6 mm, DE = 1.9 cm = 19 mm, DF = 2.9 cm = 29 mm, DG = 4.6 cm = 46 mm, EF = 1 cm = 10 mm, EG = 2.6 cm = 26 mm, FG = 1.6 cm = 16 mm
9. A. A medicine cup holds about five milliliters.
   B. My palm is about 80 millimeters wide.
   C. My dad is exactly two meters tall.
   D. My bathtub holds about 285 liters of water.
   E. Susan's puppy's mass is less than two kilograms.
   Statements will vary.

Page 58

A. 7
B. 15
C. 13
D. 10
E. 4
F. 120
G. 145
H. 139
I. 105
J. 65

1. E
2. J
3. A
4. D
5. I
6. F
7. C
8. H
9. G
10. B

Page 59

1. A. 92°F, 33°C
   B. 18°F, −8°C
   C. 60°F, 16°C
   Answers will vary.
2.

Before		After
1:45	2:30	3:15
5:05	5:50	6:35
11:20	12:05	12:50
10:40	11:25	12:10
5:20	6:05	6:50
2:55	3:40	4:25
12:35	1:20	2:05

3. A. 30°C
   B. 10°C
   C. 35°F
   D. 110°F
   E. 10°C
   Bumper stickers will vary.
4. Answers will vary.
6. Carl leaves home at 1:00. Carl gets to the theater at 1:30. Carl gets his snacks at 1:45. The previews start at 1:52. The movie starts at 2:10. Carl leaves at 4:25.
7. Fahrenheit scale should show freezing at 32° and boiling at 212°; Celsius scale should show freezing at 0° and boiling at 100°.
8. Story problems will vary.
   A. 3:55 AM
   B. 3:22 AM
   C. 6:30 AM
   D. 8:06 PM
9.

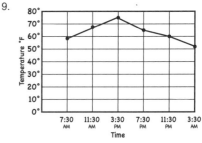

Page 60

A. 1 hour, 50 minutes
B. 3 hours, 12 minutes
E. 2 hours, 31 minutes
F. 2 hours, 28 minutes
H. 1 hour, 25 minutes
I. 1 hour, 45 minutes
L. 57 minutes
M. 2 hours, 48 minutes
O. 55 minutes
R. 2 hours, 30 minutes
S. 43 minutes
T. 1 hour, 40 minutes
V. 2 hours, 11 minutes
X. 29 minutes
Y. 2 hours, 10 minutes

<u>THEY ARE VERY FLEXIBLE!</u>

Page 61

Answers for 1, 2, 4, 6, and 8 will vary.

3. A.   B.   C.   D.

7. A. six congruent squares
   B. two congruent circles
   C. one rectangle, four triangles
   D. two congruent rectangles, four congruent rectangles
   E. two congruent triangles, three congruent rectangles

9. Figure 1 edges: HJ, HI, HK, HL, IJ, IL, JK, KL
   Figure 1 faces: LIJK, KHJ, KHL, HLI, HIJ
   Figure 2 edges: QR, QT, QU, RV, RS, VW, VU, SW, WX, ST, TX, XU
   Figure 2 faces: QTSR, SRVW, TSWX, QTXU, QUVR, XUVW

Page 62

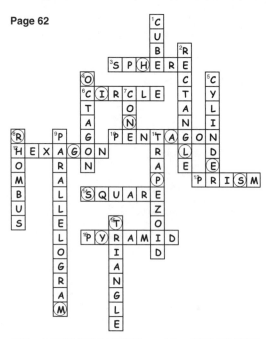

Without GEOMETRY, MATH would be "POINT-LESS"!

Page 63

Answers for 1, 6, 8, and 9 will vary.

2. A and D are congruent; B and C are similar.
3. Vertical lines of symmetry: *T, A, O, I*
   Horizontal lines of symmetry: *E, O, I, D*
   No lines of symmetry: *R, P, Z*
4. There are 6 lines of symmetry in a regular hexagon. There are 8 lines of symmetry in a regular octagon.
7. A. rotation
   B. reflection
   C. translation
   D. rotation
   E. reflection

Page 64

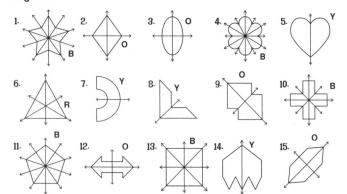

Page 65

Answers for 2, 3, and 9 will vary.

1. parallel line segments: AC, BD, GI
   perpendicular line segments: EH, AC; EH, BD; EH, GI
   intersecting line segments: FJ, GI, EH
4. Drawings will vary.

A.   B.   C.

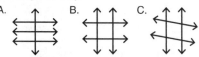

6.

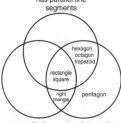

7. A, V, W, X, and Y have intersecting line segments.
   F, H, and I have parallel and perpendicular line segments.
   L and T have perpendicular line segments.
   M, N, and Z have parallel and intersecting line segments.
8. A. parallel   B. perpendicular   C. line segment   D. intersect

Page 66

1. Memorial Highway
2. Avenue C
3. Avenue C, Hillside Drive
4. Main Street, Birch Street
5. Main Street
6. Birch Street
7. no; Explanations will vary.
8. Main Street, Chase Road, Birch Street, Memorial Highway, Hillside Drive, and Highland Avenue
9. Main Street, Birch Street
10. Main Street, Birch Street
11. yes; Explanations will vary.
12. Answers will vary.

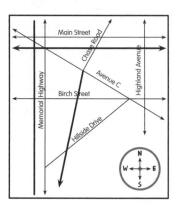

Page 67

Answers for 1, 2, 4, 6, and 8 will vary.

3. A. parallelogram or rhombus
   B. equilateral triangle
   C. trapezoid
   D. right triangle
   E. square
7. Answers will vary.
   A. Two of a trapezoid's sides are parallel.
   B. A square has four right angles.
   C. A rhombus is a parallelogram with sides that are all equal lengths.
   D. A rectangle is a parallelogram with four right angles.

9. A.   B.   C.

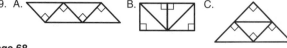

Page 68

1. acute
2. trapezoid
3. square
4. rectangle
5. isosceles
6. rhombus
7. equilateral
8. scalene
9. parallelogram
10. obtuse

11–14. Answers will vary but should include the terms *angle*, *parallel*, *quadrilateral*, and *triangle*.

They are too high maintenance!

Page 69

1. Flight E departs at 7:33. Flight F departs at 7:42. Flight I departs at 8:15. The interval between flight times increases by one minute for each successive flight.
2. H = 16, P = 32, W = 46
3.
   A.
   B. AB, FG, LM, ~~RS~~, UV, YZ
   C. 5, 15, 25, ~~35~~, 45, 55
   D. ♫♫♪♩♫♫♪♩♪♩
4. Answers will vary.
6. s
7. 960 pennies, $19.05
8. six games
9. day 14, 7 miles

Page 70

E. ◯; There is a repeating pattern of one triangle, two squares, and one circle.
K. 34; Add seven.
T. ▦; The shaded section moves clockwise.
A. ▭; The circles increase by one and the bar rotates 90 degrees.
Y. 17; Add one, then two, then three, then four, then five, and so on.
I. 121; Add 11, 22, 33, 44, and so on.
H. ∩∪; The dot moves from the left, to the middle, to the right, and then starts at the left again.
M. 48; Divide by two.
C. ◿; The shaded section moves counterclockwise.
O. ⌇; The shape is horizontal and then vertical. The dot moves separately from the left, to the middle, and then to the right in the horizontal and the vertical shapes.
U. 33; Add five and then subtract two.
S. ✕; There is a repeating pattern of one square, a diagonal, two squares, and an X.
D. 46; Add three, six, nine, and so on.
P. ∧∧; One diagonal line is added in the opposite direction.

THEY'D MAKE "POP" MUSIC!

Page 71

1. 97.8, 98.9, 100.0, 101.1, 102.2, 103.3, 104.4, 105.5, 106.6; Add 1.1.
2. 25 toothpicks
3. Row 5, nine dots; Row 10, 19 dots; Row 12, 23 dots; Add two dots.
4. 220 band members
6. 4 miles, 5.9 miles
7. A. 87.5, 85, 82.5
   B. 1,080; 7,560; 60,480
   C. 18.5, 25, 32.5
   Students' patterns will vary.
8. C. Rule: Multiply by 5 and then divide by 10; The 45 should be 1.5.
   D. Rule: Divide by 6 and then multiply by 9; The second 6 should be 9.
9. Answers will vary.

Page 72

1. 55, 64; K
2. 324, 972; C
3. 48, 6; J
4. 16, 16; F
5. 17, 77; N
6. 80, 90; H
7. 3,000; 120; D
8. 72, 47; L
9. 40, 240; B
10. 118, 121; A
11. 334; 284; G
12. 20, 20; M
13. 650, 1,625; E
14. 98, 100; I
15. 7, 9; O

Page 73

1. $8 \times 21 = 168$, $8 \times 33 = 264$; Students' columns will vary.
2. 13, 14, 15, 16, 17, 18, 19; Students' inequalities will vary.
3. b = 4, c = 8, d = 7, e = 8, f = 9
4. Steps will vary.
6. r = 13, s = 15, p = 16, q = 14
7. n = 78
8. b = 6

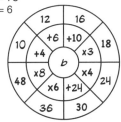

9.

	n = 9	n = 15	n = 27
A	63	105	189
B	51	81	141
C	28	30	34
D	135	225	405

Page 74

1. F
2. O
3. T
4. A
5. E
6. R
7. H
8. L
9. I
10. Y
11. K
12. W
13. B
14. V
15. G

HE BROKE THE LAW OF GRAVITY.

Page 75

Answers for 1, 7, 8, and 9 will vary.
2. range, 8 push-ups; median, 10.5 push-ups; mode, 8 push-ups

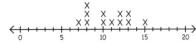

3. Explanations will vary.

Number of Students Riding Bus 12
```
1 | 4 8
2 | 0 4 9
3 | 0 4
4 | 0 5 9
5 | 2 4
```

4. Students' Favorite Fast Food

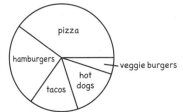

Students' Favorite Fast Food

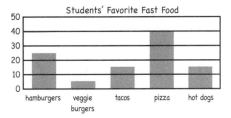

Answers will vary.

6. range, 75 minutes; mode, 45 minutes; median, 45 minutes; mean, 50 minutes

Page 76

Pounds Lifted in Bench Press Contest

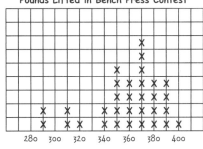

1. 400
2. nine
3. five
4. 18
5. 110
6. 370
7. 365
8. 32
9. 358 R4, or 358.125
10. Answers will vary.

Page 77

Answers for 4 and 9 will vary.
1. Conclusions will vary.

Hours of Practice
```
1 | 1 1 1 2 2 5 5 7
2 | 1 2 4 5 9
3 | 0
```

2. range = 19, median = 88.5, modes = 89, 93

Temperatures

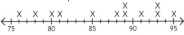

3. Answers will vary.

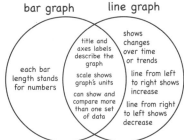

6. Line plot: **Test Scores**

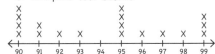

Stem-and-leaf plot:
Test Scores
```
9 | 0 0 0 0 1 1 2 3 5 5 5 5 6 7 8 9 9 9
```

7. **Track Team Results**

8. **Favorite Mascots**

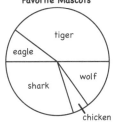

Page 78

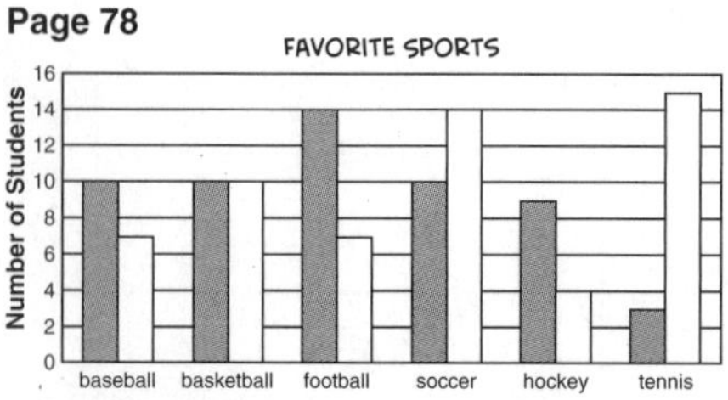

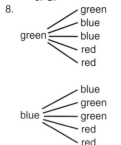

Answers for 8–10 will vary.

1. tennis
2. football
3. football and baseball
4. 12
5. tennis, soccer, basketball
6. football; baseball, basketball, and soccer
7. 56, 57

Page 79

Answers for 1–4 and 8 will vary.

6. A. median = 90, mean = 92
   B. median = 89, mean = 88
7. Explanations will vary. median = 76.5, mode = 77, range = 16
9. Diagrams will vary.
   A. 34 B. 37 C. 62.5

Page 80

1. C
2. B
3. 2
4. 4
5. 8
6. B and D
7. A and F
8. E
9. A and F
10. C

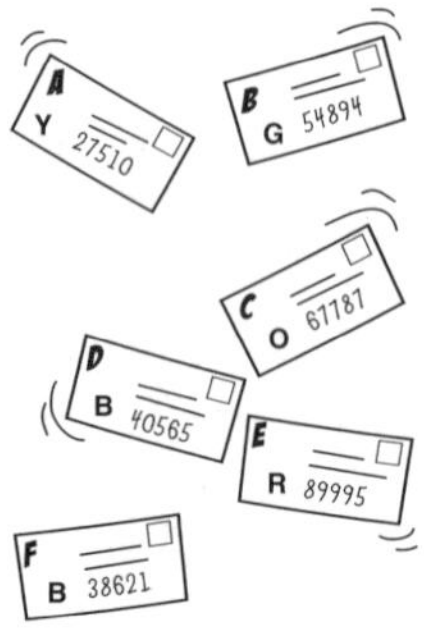

Page 81

Answers for 2–4 will vary.

1. A. 1/2 B. 1/3 C. 0 D. 1/3
6. Event C is most likely, and Event A is least likely.
7. Drawing a consonant is more likely than drawing a vowel.
   Drawing the letter *M* is more likely than drawing the letter *C*.
   Drawing the letter *M*, *T*, or *A* is more likely than drawing the letter *E*, *I*, *C*, or *S*.
8. green — green, blue, blue, red, red
   blue — blue, green, green, red, red
   red — red, green, green, blue, blue

   The likelihood of grabbing a pair of same-colored socks is 1/5.
9. A. 0/6 B. 1/3 C. 2/3

Page 82

Answers for 2, 4–8, and 15 will vary.

1. ball
3. checked ball, dotted ball
9. 4/20, or 1/5
10. 8/20, or 2/5
11. 3/20
12. 3/20
13. 12/20, or 3/5
14. 10/20, or 1/2

Page 83

1. 3 pennies, 3 nickels, 3 dimes, 3 quarters
2. (6 x 6 – 6) ÷ 6 + 6 = 11
   (7 + 7) ÷ 7 x 7 – 7 = 7
   (8 x 8 + 8) ÷ 8 – 8 = 1
3. 6 birds and 3 cats
4.

13	3	17
15	11	7
5	19	9

6. Deb's birthday is Monday, May 24; Bob's birthday is Saturday, May 22.
7. △ = 2
   ○ = 3
   □ = 4
8.

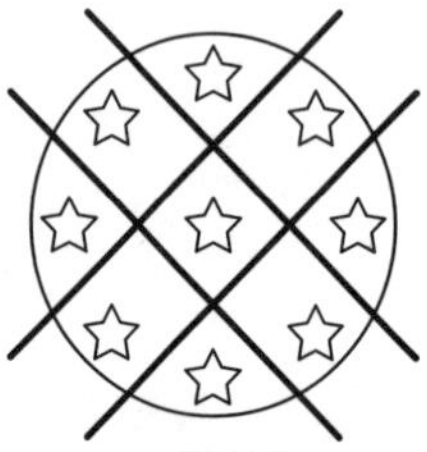

9.

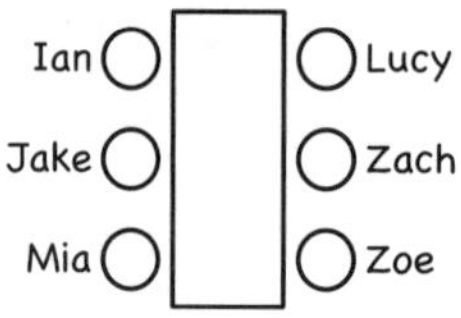

Page 84

	parrot	kitten	gerbil	dog	goldfish
Al E. Katt	O	X	X	X	X
Chip Monk	X	X	X	X	O
Earl E. Bird	X	X	O	X	X
Tom Katz	X	O	X	X	X
Gil Fish	X	X	X	O	X

	parrot	kitten	gerbil	dog	goldfish
Dolly	O	X	X	X	X
Golly	X	X	X	O	X
Kelly	X	X	X	X	O
Polly	X	X	O	X	X
Gelly	X	O	X	X	X

11. parrot, Dolly
12. goldfish, Kelly
13. gerbil, Polly
14. kitten, Gelly
15. dog, Golly

Page 85

1. hamster, Frisky; cat, Sam; fish, Sonny; dog, Theo
2. (9 + 8 + 7) ÷ 6 x 5 = 20
   (9 – 8) + 7 x (6 + 5) = 78
3. largest: 867,687
   smallest: 786,768
4. Answers will vary. Possible solutions include 158 + 159 + 160 + 161 + 162 = 800 and 58 + 59 + 60 + 61 + 62 = 300
6. Answers will vary. One possible solution is

0	10	20	30	40
10	0	40	20	30
40	30	10	0	20
20	40	30	10	0
30	20	0	40	10

7. 142,857 x 2 = 285,714
   142,857 x 3 = 428,571
   142,857 x 4 = 571,428
   142,857 x 5 = 714,285
   142,857 x 6 = 857,142
   Each product contains the digits 142,857, maintaining the digits' order in various place values.
8. 9
9. A. Answers will vary.
   B. Answers will vary.
   C. purple

Page 86

1. 9 x 4 ÷ 3 x 8 = 96
2. 4 x12 x 6 ÷ 9 = 32
3. 6 x 3 ÷ 2 x 8 = 72
4. 8 x 9 x 6 ÷ 4 = 108
5. 20 ÷ 5 x 1 x 6 = 24
6. 5 x 4 ÷ 2 x 5 = 50
7. 4 x 25 ÷ 5 ÷ 10 = 2
8. 36 ÷ 2 x 6 ÷ 3 = 36
9. 24 ÷ 6 x 12 ÷ 16 = 3
10. 8 x 35 ÷ 40 x 15 = 105
11. 48 ÷ 6 x 8 ÷ 4 = 16
12. 13 x 6 ÷ 3 ÷ 2 = 13

Page 87

1. 42, 63, 156
2. Answers will vary.

12	27	6
9	15	21
24	3	18

3. A. 7,337
   B. 484
   C. 7,117
   D. 7,117
   E. 1,881
4. A. (65 x 7) + 4 = 459
   B. (56 x 4) + 7 = 231
   C. (54 x 7) + 6 = 384
6. 35 > 21
7. Answers will vary.
   A. 28 + 7 – 6 = 29
   B. (2 + 8) x (8 + 7) = 150
   C. (2 + 8 ÷ 8) x 7 = 21
8. 408 ÷ 6 = 68
   3,915 ÷ 27 = 145
9.

7	7	7	13	34
0	14	7	3	24

Page 88

A. 9, 8, 7
B. 6, 7, 8
C. 7, 8, 9
D. 10, 9, 8
E. 6, 7, 8
F. 6, 5, 4
G. 6, 5, 4
H. 7, 6, 5
I. 5, 6, 7
J. 7, 8, 9
K. 8, 9, 10
L. 6, 5, 4
M. 8, 7, 6
N. 9, 8, 7